**BLACK BEAR CONSTRUCTION**
2236 N. W. 63rd St.
Seattle, Washington  98107
784-7609

Y0-ARS-093

# BLACK BEAR
# OF WASHINGTON

Its biology, natural history
and relationship to forest regeneration

*by*

**Richard J. Poelker**[1]

*and*

**Harry D. Hartwell**[2]

## WASHINGTON STATE GAME DEPARTMENT

**Carl N. Crouse,** *Director*          **Ralph Larson,** *Assistant Director*

**Ronald N. Andrews,** *Assistant Director*

## MEMBERS OF THE STATE GAME COMMISSION

**Arthur S. Coffin,** *Chairman*          **Glenn Galbraith**

**Elmer G. Gerken**          **Claude Bekins**

**James R. Agen**          **F. Larry Cassidy, Jr.**

**Biological Bulletin No. 14**          **September, 1973**

### Federal Aid Project W-71-R

[1]Washington State Game Department, 600 N. Capitol Way, Olympia, Wa. 98504

[2]Washington Department of Natural Resources, Land Management Center, Rt. 4, Box 490, Olympia, Wa. 98504

Permission granted to reprint or use material in this bulletin (less copyrighted material, Fig. 3 and 4) subject to full credit being given the Washington Department of Game and individual authors as necessary.

First Printing

Dedicated to the memory of Douglas J. Pierson (right), who helped plan and in-
augurate the Black Bear Research Project, and who ably lead and directed its work
for six years until his tragic death in 1969. Doug, along with cooperating U. S.
Fish and Wildlife Service Biologist, Paul Martin (left), and Army Pilot Captain
Jerry Vick, were killed in an airplane crash on August 6, 1969.

# ACKNOWLEDGMENTS

The Cooperative Black Bear Study, Federal Aid in Wildlife Restoration Project W-71-R, was a joint research effort by several state, federal and private agencies. Project leadership was provided by the Washington Department of Game. Contributing agencies were the Washington Department of Natural Resources, Washington Forest Protection Association, U.S. Fish and Wildlife Service, U.S. Forest Service, Weyerhaeuser Company, Washington State University and the University of Washington. Project headquarters was located at the Forest Land Management Center, Department of Natural Resources, Olympia, Washington. The majority of data collection was conducted from 1963 through 1969.

Gratitude is expressed for all those who contributed of time and effort to the success of this project. Particular thanks are due project personnel Glen Anderson and Keith Guenther for their unique contributions. William Latunen, Richard Wright and Donald Dickmann gave many uncompensated hours of overtime. The project is deeply indebted to Marvin Jones for exceptional enthusiasm and assistance in various phases of the field work. Special thanks are due many. Paul Martin and Wendell Dodge, U.S. Fish and Wildlife Service, provided leadership in development of radio telemetry work. Boyd Church and Leonard Milton, Washington Department of Natural Resources, gave excellent service in development of radio telemetry equipment. Bernie Pacque, Ralph Flowers, Floyd Thornton, Jack Aldrich, Jack Rotschy and Doyle DeMoss provided invaluable services in the collection of biological samples. Dr. M. S. Radwan, U.S. Forest Service, performed valuable investigations on the chemical properties of sapwood. Dr. William Lawrence, Weyerhaeuser Company, conducted essential analyses of scat and stomach samples during the food habit studies. Blood serum analyses were done by Dr. John Halver, U.S. Fish and Wildlife Service. Dr. Charles Jonkel, now with the Canadian Wildlife Service, analyzed reproductive tracts collected during the study. Frances Lombard, U.S. Fish and Wildlife Service, identified fungi in bear-damaged trees. Donald Thomas, University of British Columbia, provided assistance in preparing tooth sections for cementum annuli counts. Dr. Thomas Ogle, University of Virginia, and Dr. Albert W. Erickson, University of Idaho, provided constructive editorial comments on portions of the manuscript. Dr. Keith Farrell's studies on salmon poisoning disease contribute significant new knowledge with regard to black bear. Donald Hopkins, Washington Department of Natural Resources; Burton Lauckhart, Raleigh Moreland, Garry Garrison and Lowell D. (Zeke) Parsons, Washington Game Department; and William Larson and Robert Matthews, Washington Forest Protection Association, provided administrative guidance and support throughout the study. Don Duncan and others at the Washington State Library were particularly helpful in obtaining reference material and in providing guidance in bulletin format.

Final thanks are due Kathleen Mottman, Linda Duncan and Carol Coates, Washington Department of Game, who performed the arduous task of typing, proofing, retyping and proofing again the many drafts produced during the compilation of this bulletin.

# PREFACE

This bulletin serves a two-fold purpose. First, it is a final report of the Black Bear Study, Federal Aid in Wildlife Restoration (Pittman-Robertson) Project W-71-R. This is a cooperative study begun in 1963 by state, federal and private agencies to investigate the problem of black bear damage to coniferous forests and gain new information with regard to black bear biology and populations. The project became inactive in 1969 with the death of the principal investigator. The project was reactivated in 1973 to allow for consolidation and publication of study findings. The second purpose is to provide persons concerned with black bear a useful and informative guide. Basic information concerning black bear damage to coniferous forests, biology, population and a summary of past and current management in Washington is provided. Hopefully, with this bulletin, the man in the field, whether a forester, a state wildlife agent or other, can find answers to the numerous questions and problems encountered.

# CONTENTS

# INTRODUCTION

Although the black bear (*Ursus americanus* Pallus) is one of the most important big game species in Washington, until recently very little was known about the animal. Black bear are found throughout the forested areas of Washington. His solitary habits and association with densely forested areas make him a seldom observed member of Washington's wildlife family. His status as a sought after big game trophy has changed from unprotected varmint to desirable trophy animal and back again. Hunting seasons have been both of short duration with bag limits, to year around hunting without a bag limit. Today the black bear is gaining in popularity as a sporting animal. With increased interest being focused on the black bear, it appears now that his status as a respected and valued member of the big game community is assured both now and for the future.

## MANAGEMENT HISTORY

When the Department of Game was first organized in 1933, a season of 15 days or less was established for most counties of the state, with a one bear limit in eastern Washington and a two bear limit in western Washington. The next year the western Washington limit was dropped to one bear, and this was continued on both sides of the state until 1939, when the limit in western Washington was again raised to two bear. This was continued until 1946 when the limit was lifted completely from bear in western Washington. The bag limit in eastern Washington was raised to two bear in 1953. It stayed at two bear until 1962, when it was again dropped to one bear where it has remained.

The season on bear in eastern Washington has been fairly restrictive, for many years opening only with the deer season, while more recently it has also been open through part or all of September. In western Washington a season of varying length was continued from 1933 to 1942. In 1943 the season was opened year around in all of the area west of the Cascades, and this pattern carried through to 1948 when a restricted season was again established. The season lasted only one year, and in 1949 year-round hunting was reinstituted except in the national forests of northwestern Washington where the restricted season was continued. The restricted season pattern was gradually expanded to cover several counties in this area and all national forest land in western Washington except Olympic National Forest.

## FOREST DAMAGE AS A MANAGEMENT FACTOR

By the early forties an occasional report was cropping up concerning what appeared to be bear damage to conifer tree reproduction, and by 1950 foresters were becoming quite concerned. Extensive damage was occurring, usually in understocked stands, primarily on the Olympic Peninsula. Trees from 6 to 18 inches diameter breast height (dbh) were being hit hardest, with bark being stripped off around part or all of the base of the tree either killing or seriously damaging them. It was obvious that sport hunting was not taking enough bear to prevent this type of damage.

1

The bear damage problem was brought to the attention of the Washington State Game Commission in June, 1951, by the Puget Sound Section, Society of American Foresters. A discussion of the bear damage problem was presented and a recommendation made to declare the black bear a predator in the general areas of the Olympic Peninsula where tree damage was being inflicted (Minutes, Washington State Game Commission, June 25, 1951). The Game Commission removed the bear from the game animal list and reclassified him as a predator in five counties, Clallam, Jefferson, Grays Harbor, Mason and Kitsap, in response to this request (Minutes, Washington State Game Commission, June 27, 1951). This classification was maintained until 1969 when the black bear was again classed as a game animal (Minutes, Washington State Game Commission, July, 1969).

After the black bear was removed from the game animal list in 1951, timber companies in the Olympic Peninsula area started organized control programs. These control programs were effective in reducing the damage to some degree, but they did not eliminate it. Neither did they eliminate the bear population.

It soon became evident that bear damage was not limited to the five counties where the bear had been declared a predator. Much of southwest Washington was also having the same type of problem. In this case, rather than remove the bear from the game animal list, which would have made him a non-game animal in more than half of western Washington, a system of permits for bear control activities was adopted. At first permits were issued to individual timber companies, but later, because of the mixed ownership in many areas, all control efforts were taken over by the Washington Forest Protection Association. This system of permits is being continued at the present time. Although some opposition to the system exists, it has proven to be the best solution to the damage problem to date. Further discussion of this aspect will be presented later.

In 1967 the Legislature passed a bill establishing a tag for bear hunting in the state. This law went into effect in June of that year, and all bear killed are now required to be tagged. This tag is having a definite impact on bear management. It tends to put a premium on the bear as a game animal, and appears to stimulate more bear hunting for bear hunting's sake rather than being an animal taken incidentally while hunting another species of game. Incorporated with the bear tag was a report card the hunter is requested to fill out and return to the Game Department after killing a bear. Although the return from this card has been low, those returned have yielded information valuable to the bear management program.

Although bear damage has been recognized as a problem for many years by both foresters and game managers, both have been handicapped in trying to find a solution by a lack of knowledge concerning the animal, and also by a lack of information concerning long-term effects of bear damage on timber reproduction. In an attempt to gain some answers to these questions, the Department of Game established a cooperative black bear research project starting in 1963. Involved in the project with the Department of Game were the Washington State Department of Natural Resources, Bureau of Sport Fish-

2

eries and Wildlife, U. S. Forest Service and private industry. The major goal of the project was to obtain information upon which a more objective bear management program could be based. Both the general biology of the black bear and its relationship to forest regeneration were studied.

One outgrowth of the study, which is having a significant impact on bear management, is a growing interest in sport hunting as a means of controlling bear damage. A pilot study on three areas in southwest Washington in 1964 showed that sport hunting was effective in controlling bear damage in one of the areas, but had little effect on the other two. This concept of sport hunting as a control on bear damage is again being considered. A program is currently being implemented that will put increased sport hunting pressure on specific bear damage areas. A full discussion of this program will be presented later in the Management Section. The history of hunting seasons and game status for black bear in Washington is shown in Table 1.

## COOPERATIVE BLACK BEAR STUDY OBJECTIVES

Objectives of the Cooperative Black Bear Study, listed below, are contained in the "Preliminary Project Statement", Federal Aid to Wildlife Restoration Project W-71-R, June 14, 1963.

The primary objective of the study was to develop techniques for the management of the black bear in Washington.

Secondary objectives were:
1. To determine why black bear feed on the sapwood or inner portion of the bark of coniferous trees.
2. To determine the population densities of black bear in the various forest types and forest successional stages.
3. To study distribution patterns, and the effect of food supplies on these patterns.
4. To examine and evaluate the available information concerning food habits of black bear. Field studies and controlled feeding experiments were to be conducted.
5. To study the effect of hunter harvest and/or control measures on black bear populations, and determine the maximum allowable harvest consistent with good game management principles.

As in any long-term study, particularly one with changes in supervisory and investigative personnel, these objectives were subjected to modification, deletion and addition as the investigation progressed. Some of these original objectives have been answered in total or in part, while others have been dropped or modified. This is a natural result of encountering investigative roadblocks, changing priorities, acquisition of new information, either from the study or current literature, and refinement of the study as it progressed.

**TABLE 1.—General black bear seasons and bag limits, eastern and western Washington—1950 to 1973.**

| Year | BAG LIMIT | | GENERAL SEASONS | |
|---|---|---|---|---|
| | Eastern | Western | Eastern | Western |
| 1950 | 1 | No Limit | Deer Season | Year-round[a] |
| 1951[b] | 1 | No Limit | Deer Season[c] | Year-round[a] |
| 1952[b] | 1 | No Limit | Deer Season[c] | Year-round[a] |
| 1953[b] | 2 | No Limit | Deer Season[c] | Year-round[a] |
| 1954[b] | 2 | No Limit | Deer Season[c] | Year-round[a] |
| 1955[b] | 2 | No Limit | Deer Season[c] | Year-round[ad] |
| 1956[b] | 2 | No Limit | Deer Season[c] | Year-round[ad] |
| 1957[b] | 2 | No Limit | Deer Season[c] | Year-round[ad] |
| 1958[b] | 2 | No Limit | Deer Season[c] | Year-round[ae] |
| 1959[b] | 2 | No Limit | Deer Season[c] | Year-round[ae] |
| 1960[b] | 2 | No Limit | Deer Season[c] | Year-round[ae] |
| 1961[b] | 2 | No Limit | Deer Season[c] | **Aug. 1** to **Nov. 1,** outside of NF in King and Snohomish. **Sept. 9** to **Nov. 1,** in Skagit and Whatcom, inside NF in Snohomish, King, Pierce and Lewis and part of Pinchot NF. **Year-round** in rest of west side. |
| 1962[b] | 1[f] | No Limit | **Sept. 1** to **Nov. 7** in Kittitas and part of Yakima, **Sept. 1** to **Nov. 10,** in Chelan and Okanogan, **Sept. 15** to **Nov. 7** in Asotin, Columbia, Garfield and Walla Walla, **Sept. 15** to **Nov. 10,** in Ferry, Stevens, Pend Oreille and Spokane, **Oct. 13** to **Nov. 7,** in rest of east side. | **Sept. 8** to **Nov. 4,** in Whatcom and NF lands of Skagit, Snohomish, King, Pierce and part of Lewis, **Aug. 1** to **Nov. 4,** in Skagit, Snohomish and King outside NF. **Year-round** in rest of west side.[c] |
| 1963[b] | 1[f] | No Limit | **Mar. 1** to **Apr. 30,** in Asotin, Columbia, Ferry, Garfield, Pend Oreille, Spokane, Stevens and Walla Walla. **Sept. 7** to **Nov. 6,** in all of east side, except **Nov. 10** in Ferry, Stevens, Pend Oreille, Spokane, Chelan and Okanogan. | **July 1** to **Nov. 3,** outside the NF in Skagit, Snohomish, King and Whatcom, and **Sept. 7** to **Nov. 3,** inside the NF. **Year-round** in rest of west side. |

**TABLE 1.**
(cont'd.)

| Year | BAG LIMIT | | GENERAL SEASONS | |
|------|-----------|---------|-----------------|---------|
| | Eastern | Western | Eastern | Western |
| 1964[b] | 1 | No Limit | **Sept. 8** to **Nov. 11,** except to **Nov. 4** in Asotin, Benton, Columbia, Garfield, Kittitas, Walla Walla and Yakima. | **July 1** to **Nov. 1,** outside the NF in Skagit, Snohomish, King and Whatcom and **Sept. 12** to **Nov. 1** inside NF. **Year-round** in remainder. |
| 1965[b] | 1 | No Limit | **Sept. 1** to **Nov. 14,** in Ferry, Pend Oreille, Spokane and Stevens, **Sept. 11** to **Nov. 10,** in Asotin, Benton, Columbia, Garfield, Kittitas, Walla Walla and Yakima. **Sept. 11** to **Nov. 14** in remainder. | **July 1** to **Nov. 7,** outside the NF in Skagit, Snohomish, King and Whatcom, and **Sept. 11** to **Nov. 7** inside NF. **Year-round** in remainder. |
| 1966[b] | 1[f] | No Limit | **Sept. 10** to **Nov. 13,** except only to **Nov. 5** in Asotin, Benton, Columbia, Garfield, Kittitas, Walla Walla and Yakima. | **July 1** to **Nov. 5** outside the NF in Snohomish and King, **Aug. 1** to **Nov. 5** outside the NF in Skagit and Whatcom, and inside the NF in all 4 counties **Sept. 10** to **Nov. 5.** **Year-round** in remainder. |
| 1967[b] (Bear Tag Required) | 1 | No Limit | **Sept. 9** to **Nov. 12,** except only to **Nov. 5** in Asotin, Benton, Columbia, Garfield, Kittitas, Walla Walla and Yakima. | **Aug. 1** to **Nov. 5** outside the NF in King, Snohomish, Skagit and Whatcom, **Sept. 9** to **Nov. 5** inside the NF in Skagit, King, Snohomish, Whatcom, Pierce, Lewis, Skamania and part of Klickitat, **Apr. 1** to **Nov. 5** outside the NF in Pierce, Lewis, and Skamania, and in all of Clark, Cowlitz, Pacific, Thurston and Wahkiakum. **Year-round** in remainder. |

**TABLE 1.**
(cont'd.)

| Year | BAG LIMIT | | GENERAL SEASONS | |
|------|-----------|----------|-----------------|---------|
| | Eastern | Western | Eastern | Western |
| 1968[b] | 1 | No Limit | **Sept. 7** to **Nov. 11** except only to **Nov. 5** in Asotin, Benton, Columbia, Garfield, Kittitas, Walla Walla and Yakima. | **July 1** to **Nov. 5** outside the NF in King and Snohomish, **Aug. 1** to **Nov. 5** outside the NF in Skagit and Whatcom, **Sept. 7** to **Nov. 5** inside the NF in Skagit, King, Snohomish, Whatcom, Lewis, Skamania and part of Klickitat, **Apr. 1** to **Nov. 5** outside the NF in Pierce, Lewis and Skamania and in all of Clark, Cowlitz, Pacific, Thurston and Wahkiakum. **Year-round** in remainder. |
| 1969 (Removed from predator status in Clallam, Jefferson, Grays Harbor, Kitsap and Mason counties) | 1 | No Limit | **Sept. 6** to **Nov. 9** except only to **Nov. 2** in Asotin, Benton, Columbia, Garfield, Kittitas, Walla Walla and Yakima. | **July 1** to **Nov. 2** outside the NF in King and Snohomish, **Aug. 1** to **Nov. 2** outside the NF in Skagit and Whatcom, **Sept. 6** to **Nov. 2** inside the NF in Skagit, Snohomish, King, Whatcom, Pierce, Lewis, Skamania and part of Klickitat, **Apr. 1** to **Nov. 2** outside the NF in Pierce, Lewis and Skamania and in all of Clark, Cowlitz, Pacific, Thurston, and Wahkiakum. **Year-round** in remainder. |
| 1970 | 1 | No Limit except 3 per year in King, Skagit, Snohomish and Whatcom. | **Sept. 12** to **Oct. 11** in Ferry, Lincoln, Pend Oreille, Spokane, Stevens and Whitman, **Sept. 12** to **Nov. 8** in remainder. | **Apr. 1** to **Nov. 8** outside the NF in Lewis, Pierce and Skamania, and in all of Clallam, Clark, Cowlitz, Grays Harbor, Jefferson, Kitsap, Mason, Pacific, Thurston and Wahkiakum. |

6

**TABLE 1.**
(cont'd.)

| Year | BAG LIMIT | | GENERAL SEASONS | |
| | Eastern | Western | Eastern | Western |
|------|---------|---------|---------|---------|
| | | | | **July 1** to **Nov. 8** outside the NF and Ross Lake NRA in King, Skagit, Snohomish and Whatcom. **Sept. 12** to **Nov. 8** inside the NF and Ross Lake NRA in King, Lewis, Pierce, Skagit, Skamania, Snohomish, Whatcom and part of Klickitat. |
| 1971 | 1 | No Limit except 2 per year in King, Skagit, Snohomish and Whatcom. | **Sept. 11** to **Oct. 17** in Ferry, Lincoln, Pend Oreille, Spokane, Stevens and Whitman, **Sept. 11** to **Nov. 11** in Adams, Chelan, Douglas, Franklin, Grant and Okanogan. **Sept. 11** to **Nov. 14** in Asotin, Benton, Columbia, Garfield, Kittitas, Walla Walla and Yakima. | **Apr. 1** to **Oct. 30** outside the NF in Lewis, Pierce and Skamania and in all of Clark, Clallam, Cowlitz, Grays Harbor, Jefferson, Kitsap, Mason, Pacific, Thurston and Wahkiakum, **July 1** to **Oct. 30** outside the NF and Ross Lake NRA in King, Skagit, Snohomish and Whatcom, **Sept. 11** to **Oct. 30** inside the NF and Ross Lake NRA in King, Lewis, Pierce, Skagit, Skamania, Snohomish, Whatcom and part of Klickitat. |
| 1972 | 1 | No Limit except 2 per year in King, Skagit, Snohomish and Whatcom. | **Sept. 9** to **Oct. 28.** | **Apr. 1** to **Oct. 28** outside the NF in Lewis, Pierce and Skamania and in all of Clallam, Clark, Cowlitz, Grays Harbor, Jefferson, Kitsap, Mason, Pacific, Thurston and Wahkiakum. **July 1** to **Oct. 28** outside the NF and Ross Lake NRA in King, Skagit, Snohomish and Whatcom, **Sept. 9** to **Oct. 28** inside |

TABLE 1.
(cont'd.)

| Year | BAG LIMIT | | GENERAL SEASONS | |
| | Eastern | Western | Eastern | Western |
| --- | --- | --- | --- | --- |
| | | | | NF and Ross Lake NRA in King, Lewis, Pierce, Skagit, Skamania, Snohomish and Whatcom. |
| 1973 | 1 | No Limit except 2 per year in King, Skagit, Snohomish and Whatcom. | Sept. 8 to Oct. 31. | Apr. 1 to June 30 in spring bear management units, July 1 to Oct. 31 outside the NF and Ross Lake NRA in King, Skagit, Snohomish, Whatcom, Lewis, Pierce and Skamania, and in all of Clallam, Clark, Cowlitz, Grays Harbor, Jefferson, Kitsap, Mason, Pacific, Thurston and Wahkiakum; Sept. 8 to Oct. 31 inside the NF and Ross Lake NRA in King, Lewis, Pierce, Skagit, Skamania, Snohomish and Whatcom. |

[a] During the deer season only in Mt. Baker, Snoqualmie, and parts of Gifford Pinchot National Forest (NF).
[b] Declared a predator in Clallam, Grays Harbor, Jefferson, Kitsap and Mason counties.
[c] Special season in selected areas also exists.
[d] Special season in Skagit and Whatcom counties.
[e] Special season in Skagit, Whatcom and Snohomish counties.
[f] Closed to the taking of cubs and/or females accompanied by cubs in certain areas and/or seasons.

## BLACK BEAR CLASSIFICATION AND DISTRIBUTION

Scientific classification of the black bear places it in the following taxonomic categories: Class—Mammalia, Order—Carnivora, Family—Ursidae, Genus—*Ursus,* Species—*americanus.* Thus, black bear are in the same genus as grizzly bear (*Ursus arctos* Linneaus), but are related to polar bear (*Thalarctos maritimus* Phipps) only by family. *Ursus* spp. and *Thalarctos* sp. represent the family Ursidae in North America (Hall and Kelson 1959). Two subspecies of black bear are recognized in Washington (op. cit.). They are *U. a. altifrontalis* Elliot, and *U. a. cinnamomum* Audubon and Bachman. Dental formulae for deciduous and permanent dentition in the black bear are i$\frac{3}{3}$ c$\frac{1}{1}$ p$\frac{3}{3}$ and I$\frac{3}{3}$ C$\frac{1}{1}$ P$\frac{4}{4}$ M$\frac{2}{2}$ respectively (Rausch 1961). Dentition of adult and cub black bear are shown in Figures 1 and 2.

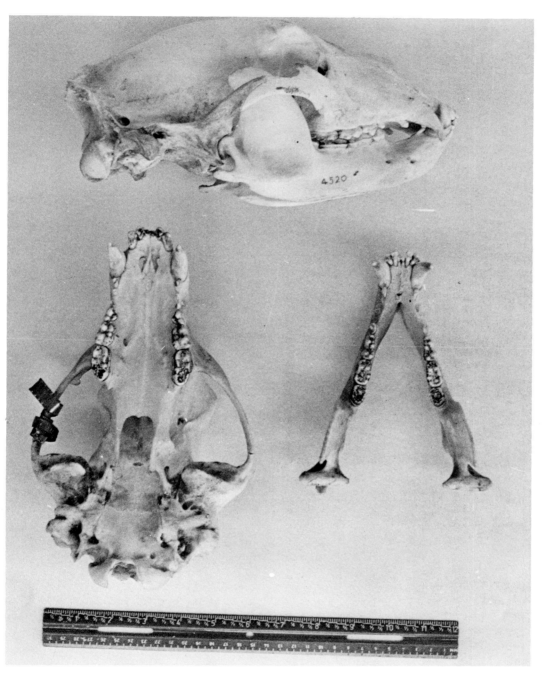

**FIG. 1.—Adult black bear skull.**

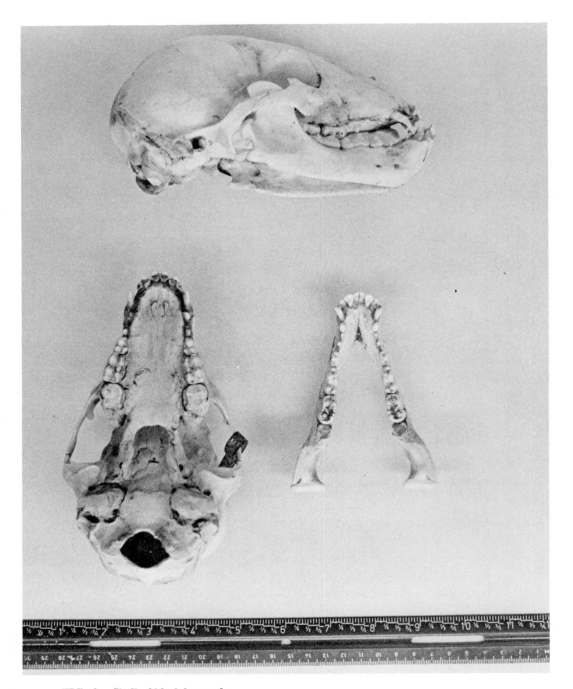

**FIG. 2.—Skull of black bear cub.**

Distribution of the type species, *Ursus americanus* Pallus, extends from central Mexico through eastern North America to the arctic slope in Alaska (Hall and Kelson 1959; Walker 1968; Miller and Kellogg 1955) (Fig. 3). In Washington, the most abundant and widespread subspecies is *U. a. altifrontalis* Elliot, which ranges from the east slopes of the Cascade Mountains

*Ursus americanus*

| | | |
|---|---|---|
| 1. *U.a. altifrontalis* | 7. *U.a. emmonsii* | 13. *U.a. luteolus* |
| 2. *U.a. amblyceps* | 8. *U.a. eremicus* | 14. *U.a. machetes* |
| 3. *U.a. americanus* | 9. *U.a. floridanus* | 15. *U.a. perniger* |
| 4. *U.a. californiensis* | 10. *U.a. hamiltoni* | 16. *U.a. pugnax* |
| 5. *U.a. carlottae* | 11. *U.a. hunteri* | 17. *U.a. randi* |
| 6. *U.a. cinnamomum* | 12. *U.a. kermodei* | 18. *U.a. vancouveri* |

FIG. 3.- - Black bear distribution in North America (From Hall and Kelson, The Mammals of North America, 1959, The Ronald Press Co.,New York.)

11

throughout western Washington to the coast (Fig. 4), southerly through Oregon into northern California along the coast, and north into British Columbia (Hall and Kelson 1959). Northeastern Washington and the Blue Mountains of southeast Washington are inhabited by *U. a. cinnamomum* Audubon and Bachman (Fig. 4), whose range includes eastern Oregon, Idaho, western Montana and Wyoming and parts of Colorado, Utah and Nevada (op. cit.). Black bear typically inhabit forested areas throughout their range. Type specimen for *U. a. altifrontalis* is from Lake Crescent, Clallam County, Washington, and for *U. a. cinnamomum,* Lower Clearwater River, Clearwater County, in western Idaho. Other subspecies account for the presence of black bear in all 48 conterminous states and provinces of Canada. Subsequent reference to the black bear in the text will be to species level only unless otherwise indicated.

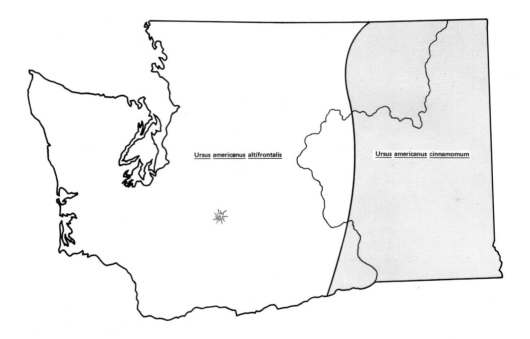

FIG. 4.- - Distribution of Ursus americanus altifrontalis and Ursus americanus cinnamomum in Washington (From Hall and Kelson, The Mammals of North America, 1959, The Ronald Press Co., New York.)

12

# STUDY AREA

## SELECTION CRITERIA

The selection of a primary study area for detailed field work was restricted by the need to have an area which, while comparable in vegetation, successional stage and geographic characteristics, contained areas with and without significant bear damage. Further requirements such as ease of access and abundant bear populations placed additional restrictions on the selection.

Population, management and harvest data have been gathered on a state-wide basis. Information regarding the relationship of black bear to forest regeneration, including vegetation surveys, damage transects, tagging, radio tracking and food habit studies, has been collected, for the most part, on the primary study area in Grays Harbor County, Washington. Information on anatomical characteristics, incidence and history of bear damage and tree species preferences of black bear with respect to forest damage, reflects data collected in and outside of the primary study area. Data collected outside of the primary study area were mainly from western Washington, but occasionally from other western states and provinces of Canada.

## DESCRIPTION OF STUDY AREA

The area selected is in eastern Grays Harbor County, Washington, lying north and south of the Chehalis River (Fig. 5). This area met the requirements for field work with bear damage present north of the river and no bear damage recorded south of the river. Four townships north of the river were designated as the damage study area, and one township south of the river was designated as the non-damage or control study area (Fig. 6). Bear control efforts had been existent on the damage area since the early 1950's.

Maximum elevations for the study area are under 3000 feet. Most of the area lies below 2000 feet. Annual rainfall is between 55 and 85 inches. The general area is drained by the Chehalis River and its tributaries. The work of these tributaries has resulted in a deeply dissected maze of hills. A description of the non-damage area is given, in part, by Brown (1961). A detailed account of soil characteristics is given in a report by the Forest Soils Committee of the Douglas-fir Region (1957), and by Franklin and Dyrness (1969). This last reference also describes the vegetation zones, physiography and geology of the area. The following general description is derived from these sources.

### Soil

Most of the soils in this area fall in the *Brown Latosol* great soil group. *Brown Latosols* occurring in the Douglas-fir region have been formed with rainfall of 65 to 100 inches or more, and relatively high temperatures. The vegetation consists of dense, coniferous forest and associated shrubs, herbs and grasses. The soils were formed upon well-weathered, deep residuum ore deposits, which originated from a variety of rocks. Soils are medium acid

13

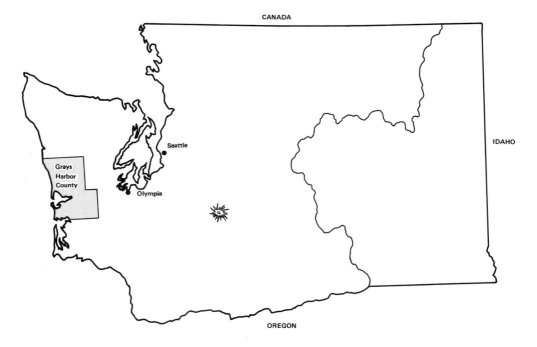

FIG. 5. - - Location of general study area in Washington.

throughout the profile. Surface soil is overlaid by a thin layer of organic debris in various stages of decomposition. The $A_1$ horizon is friable, mellow and granular, with variable amount of shot. Its color is brown to reddish-brown. A fair amount of organic matter is accumulated. As a rule there is no $A_2$ horizon, but a transitional A. The $B_2$ horizon is yellowish-red or reddish-yellow, usually fine in texture and compaction. The soil mass breaks into irregular clods. Occasionally, the $B_2$ can be subdivided on the basis of textural changes, color, compaction or the presence of shot. The soils have imperfectly developed structural peds which may be feebly coated with colloids.

## Vegetation

The study area lies in the western hemlock (*Tsuga heterophylla*) zone. This is the region where the subclimax Douglas-fir (*Pseudotsuga menziesii*) is prominent as a long-lived seral stage. This zone is essentially in agreement with Merriam's Humid Transition Zone (Barrett 1962). Dominance of Douglas-fir over much of the area is a result of repeated burns and logging. In the absence of logging or wildfire, western hemlock would eventually displace Douglas-fir as it is the more shade tolerant of the two species. Typical examples of prominent understory plants are oceanspray (*Holodiscus discolor*) on the more zeric sites, possibly in association with salal (*Gaultheria shallon*), oregon grape (*Berberis nervosa*) and vine maple (*Acer circinatum*) on mesic

14

sites, and sword fern (*Polystichum munitum*) and oxalis (*Oxalis oregana*) on the moister sites. The oceanspray—oregon grape—sword fern progression from drier to wetter sites is common throughout the western hemlock zone.

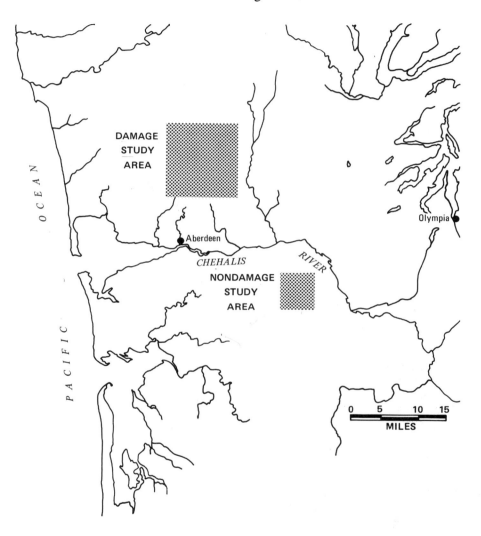

FIG. 6. - - Location of primary study areas in Grays Harbor County, western Washington.

# SECTION I

# FOREST RELATIONSHIPS

# BEAR DAMAGE

What exactly is bear damage? Damage, as referred to in this study, is peeling of bark from a tree by a black bear in order to make the sapwood layer available for consumption. Bear damage occurs primarily in the spring and early summer when most of the sapwood is layed down. Generally bark is loosened at the base of the tree and peeled upwards 2 to 3 feet, to 8 or 10 feet on occasion, leaving characteristically pointed or fusiform patterns in the remaining bark at the apex of the torn area (Fig. 7). Loosened bark is not eaten by the bear but is discarded beneath the tree. Girdling of the tree may be complete or partial. Complete girdling results in eventual death of the tree. Partial girdling may result in retarded growth, infection through the wound

**FIG. 7.—Basal scarring from bear damage on western redcedar, Clallam County, Washington, spring 1972.**

area by various fungi and subsequent rot. Trees with less than one-half of their bole circumference girdled often recover with little or no growth loss and little subsequent volume reduction. Occasionally a tree will be "frilled" with bark strips loosened at the base and pulled upwards but not completely free of the tree (Fig. 8). At times, damage occurs above the base of the tree, often far into the top (Fig. 9). Following the barking of the tree the exposed sapwood is

FIG. 8.—Bear damage to western redcedar, Clallam County, Washington, showing "frilled" effect, in spring 1972.

18

**FIG. 9.—Bear damage in top portion of Douglas-fir on Suiattle River, in Washington, 1972.**

eaten by the bear. Sapwood is removed by vertical scraping of the upper or lower incisors, leaving a pattern of vertical grooves on the trunk of the tree (Fig. 10). This vertical tooth pattern, together with the size of bark fragments, differentiates bear damage from similar attacks by other forest inhabitants such as the porcupine (*Erithizon dorsatum*) or chickaree (*Tamiasciursus douglasii*). Sapwood taken from the stomach of an adult female black bear is shown in Figure 11. Particular reasons for these attacks by black bear and their effect on trees will be discussed later. A useful guide to identification of animal damage to conifers is provided by Lawrence, et al. (1961).

19

FIG. 10.—Basal damage to western redcedar showing detail of tooth marks left by black bear.

FIG. 11.—Stomach contents of female black bear taken in May, 1972, in Clallam County, Washington, showing sapwood strips.

## DAMAGE HISTORY

*"At one season the bear may be seen examining the lower part of the trunk of a tree for several minutes with much attention, at the same time looking around and snuffing the air. It then rises on its hind legs, approaches the trunk, embraces it with the forelegs and scratches the bark with its teeth and claws for several minutes in continuance. Its jaws clash against each other until a mass of foam runs down both sides of the mouth. After this, it continues its rambles."*

The description above was written over one hundred years ago by John James Audubon.

There is no evidence that Audubon attempted to analyze this behavior. Other naturalists observed trees which had been marked by black bear and they postulated that the markings constituted some method of communication (Seton 1909). Black bear "measuring trees" or "marking trees" were observed by other classical naturalists in the major black bear areas of the East and Southeast.

In Washington, an occasional marked or damaged tree was observed in nearly all of the areas where black bear were known to occur, but because of the knowledge that black bear had always been known to mark certain trees, there was little concern. There are reports of black bear damaged trees in Grays Harbor County, Washington, shortly after the turn of the century. William G. Hulet, a lifetime resident and bear hunter, states that when he was a youngster his father showed him bear damaged trees in the Wishkah Valley. Photographs of bear damaged timber are reported to have been taken back in 1915 by Mr. T. Scheffer, a U.S. Fish and Wildlife Service biologist (Crews 1952). Bear damage has been identified back as far as 1854 in Douglas-fir trees on the Wind River Experimental Forest in Washington (Childs and Worthington 1955). In the middle 1940's, however, foresters became aware of a seemingly new development in the traditional black bear habit of marking trees: They were beginning to debark trees on an extensive scale. Apparently the first serious bear damage in Washington was noted in 1942 when heavily damaged 30 to 40-year-old Douglas-fir were reported in a small area northwest of Hoquiam in Grays Harbor County (Lauckhart 1955). Damage reports from adjacent areas in Mason County were noted by 1950 (Levin 1954). In this same period, extensive damage was reported from the northern Olympic Peninsula and southwest Washington, as well as other western states including Alaska.

Several tree damage surveys and a food habit study of the black bear were made to investigate the extent and nature of this damage problem in Washington.

A damage survey of a 3-acre clearcut in Grays Harbor County by Childs and Worthington (1955) indicated that 25 percent of live Douglas-fir over 12 inches dbh had been damaged, and that partially girdled (live trees) were three times as numerous as those completely girdled and killed. There was twice as much damage among trees 12 inches dbh and over than among smaller trees, and damage was most frequent in medium-stocked, mixed conifer types. Over most of the area, composed mainly of well-stocked and nearly pure 50-year-old western hemlock, less than 2 percent of the total trees were damaged. In this same area, however, 17 percent of the large Douglas-fir were damaged, indicating an apparent preference for this species over western hemlock.

Another study in Grays Harbor County revealed that bears were damaging trees from 6 to 15 inches dbh very heavily (Brown 1950). In part of the area studied (6 ½-acre stand), which had a low density of 60 Douglas-fir trees per acre, 54 percent were damaged and 44 percent of these damaged trees were dead from complete basal girdling. Ten percent of the damage had occurred in the current year. In another low density stand, 6 acres in size, with approximately 23 Douglas-fir trees per acre, 73 percent were damaged and 55 percent of these damaged trees were dead from complete basal girdling. Twenty-five percent of the damage occurred during the current year.

A survey by forestry students on 64,000 acres in Grays Harbor County indicated that bear were damaging the smaller classes of trees. About 30 percent of all trees over 6 inches dbh on the entire area had been damaged. Damage was particularly severe in open stands of 20 to 30-year old trees. Among trees over 6 inches dbh, 51 percent of the Douglas-fir were damaged as compared to less than one percent for other species. In one fully stocked stand of Douglas-fir damage was occurring above the rough basal bark 8 to 30 feet above ground. Although western hemlock, western redcedar (*Thuja plicata*), Sitka spruce (*Picea sitchensis*) and red alder (*Alnus rubra*) were also attacked, damage was primarily on Douglas-fir (Levin 1954).

One of the most comprehensive studies was made on a 3-acre stand of 110-year-old Douglas-fir in Skamania County, Washington, at the time it was clearcut in 1950 (Childs and Worthington 1955). Of 132 trees examined, 107 had been damaged by bear. More than two-thirds of this damage had occurred when the stand was 25 to 45 years old. Some of the trees had been damaged two to five times over a 2 to 46-year period.

Studies on Crown-Zellerbach tree farm lands near Neah Bay, Clallam County, Washington, indicated that 60 percent of the 20-year-old second-growth Douglas-fir was either damaged or killed. Nineteen percent of the trees were killed. Of the 41 percent damaged but not killed, 81 percent were more than one-half girdled. Damage in this area appeared to be restricted to the more vigorous trees and was found throughout the tree farm. Douglas-fir was the most damaged species, although silver fir (*Abies amabilis*), western hemlock and Sitka spruce were also damaged. Western hemlock was the dominant conifer in the area (Lucci 1960).

The type of injury to the tree found in these early studies varied from a small patch of bark, less than one-foot square removed, to complete girdling of the trunk. Injuries could occur on any portion of the trunk, from the ground level up to 40 to 50 feet in the crown. Although many species of conifers and some hardwoods were reported damaged, Douglas-fir appeared to be the preferred species even in areas where other conifers were dominant. There did not appear to be a definitely preferred size class in all areas, but in the areas where the larger trees were damaged, it was up in the crown where the bark

22

was thin and easy to remove. Faster growing, more vigorous trees were more susceptible to damage than slower growing ones. In the most critical areas, damage was in the areas with very light stocking. This was eliminating a possible seed source that could complete restocking of the area, and was retarding the planned rotation period (Levin 1954).

The concern of foresters and game biologists over the extent of damage resulted, as mentioned earlier, in the black bear being declared a predator in all five counties of the Olympic and Kitsap Peninsulas, and the beginning of organized bear control projects employing professional trappers in 1951. This type of control, financed by landowners sustaining damage, has been continued on a permit basis to the present time.

Conifer damage by black bear has not been restricted to Washington. Occurrences of damage have been noted in most regions where timber has been a primary industry. Lutz (1951) encountered what he referred to as a spectacular type of damage to trees in the forests of the lowlands on the Kenai Peninsula in Alaska. He found both white spruce (*Picea glauca*) and aspen (*Populus tremuloides*) damaged. Frequency of damage to spruce ranged from 10 to 20 trees per acre with most damage occurring to medium-sized trees of 10 to 18 inches dbh.

A study of basal scarring in British Columbia found most basal scars of white pine (*Pinus monticola*) to be attributable to bear damage (Molnar and McMinn 1960). While some stands were entirely free from scars, damage to as many as 42 percent of the white pine over an area of 10 acres was recorded. Individual trees of other species, such as alpine fir (*Abies lasiocarpa*) and western redcedar, were sometimes even more severely damaged than white pine. Most of the white pine examined were between 21 and 45 years old when scarring occurred. Complete girdling of white pine was uncommon. In several cases, bark from Douglas-fir 60 years old was stripped from the bole 40 feet above the ground.

Early records of black bear damage to redwood trees (*Sequoia sempervirens*) in California date back to 1936 for scattered locations in the Little River Basin of Humboldt County. Damage apparently remained at an insignificant level until about 1945 when it began to show dramatic increases with a peak damage period in about 1950. Studies were made of damage areas and much detailed information was obtained. Damaged stands were predominantly redwood with Douglas-fir and alder as associated species. Glover (1955) found black bear to be the animal responsible for the damage. He found second-growth timber 10 to 30 years old was injured most frequently. The majority of damage was found to occur in spring and early summer over a 75 to 120-day period. Average annual increment of damage was 6 percent. Average incidence of cumulative damage was 11.6 trees per acre. Approximately 48 percent of 234 freshly scarred trees had also been damaged in previous years. Fritz (1955) found the more limby trees to be more frequently damaged.

Damage was reported in Maine on balsam fir (*Abies balsamea*), red spruce (*Picea rubens*) and northern white cedar (*Thuja occidentalis*/ *Cupressus thyoides*) (species not stated in reference) (Zeedyk 1957). Balsam fir was preferred. Large pole-size and small saw-timber size trees were most frequently damaged. No damage was found on other conifer or deciduous species in this area.

Damage to alpine fir, western larch (*Larix occidentalis*), whitebark pine (*Pinus albicaulis*) and Douglas-fir was reported in Montana by Jonkel (1962). Girdled lodgepole pine (*Pinus contorta*) were reported by Jonkel (1971) near Big Creek in Montana. The killing of large numbers of lodgepole pine by black bear was credited with helping to keep the important winter range of moose (*Alces alces*) in a seral state of lodgepole pine and willow (*Salix* spp.), rather than allowing it to proceed to a climax community less suitable for moose.

Moore (1940) reported damage to Douglas-fir dating from 1935 on the Mt. Hebo tree plantation in Oregon, where up to 2 percent of the trees were damaged. Crouch (1969) reported some bear damage in the west-central Cascades.

Reports of bear damage to lodgepole pine have been received for areas in Targhee National Forest in northwestern Wyoming. One of the project investigators had noted bear damage to lodgepole pine in this same area while working there. Reports of grizzly bear feeding on sapwood upon emerging from hibernation were also received (Pierson, pers. comm.).

## DAMAGE CHARACTERISTICS

A thorough knowledge of the geographical areas of black bear damage and the characteristics of this damage are essential to any comprehensive study of the relationships between black bear and coniferous forests. General damage characteristics known and recorded prior to this study are:
1.  Damage is primarily to immature, smooth-barked trees.
2.  Certain species of trees are damaged more frequently than others.
3.  Faster growing, more vigorous trees are apparently more frequently damaged than slower growing trees.
4.  Bear damage does not occur in all apparently susceptible timber stands.

As these early observations were limited in scope, it was determined that information covering all of western Washington was needed. More observations, including those from areas not normally thought of as being damage areas were required to reveal additional facts concerning damage characteristics and to disclose damage trends heretofore unidentified.

A damage questionnaire (Appendix A) was determined to be the only practical method of obtaining this information. A questionnaire was designed and sent to people directly involved in the management of extensive tracts of forest land throughout western Washington and the southern one-half of the east slope of the Cascade Mountains. The questionnaire requested the following basic information:
1.  Geographical distribution of bear damage.
2.  Occurrence of bear in non-damage areas.
3.  Predominant timber size of area reported.
4.  Species, age and dbh of damaged trees.

5. Variations of damage intensity between stands of different site quality and stocking density.
6. Tree species which were damaged most frequently.
7. Past history of bear damage in area reported .

Maps were requested from the areas reporting damage, showing the known boundaries of current damage and special identification of tracts where damage exceeded 25 percent of the stand.

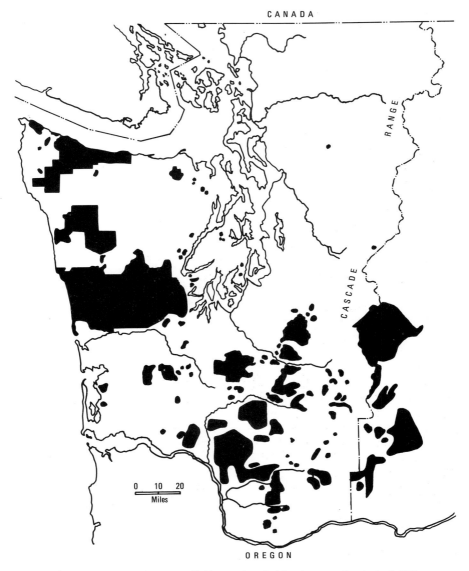

FIG. 12. - - Distribution of bear damage in western Washington as determined from damage questionnaire data in 1963.

Seventy-seven questionnaires were sent out, and 73 were returned. Returns included 27 from management units of 14 major timber companies, 19 from administrative districts and honor camps of the State of Washington Department of Natural Resources, 23 from ranger districts of Mount Baker, Snoqualmie and Gifford Pinchot National Forests, and 4 from bear control personnel. Forty-nine of the questionnaires included maps which were used to prepare a composite map of the distribution and intensity of existing bear damage in western Washington (Fig. 12).

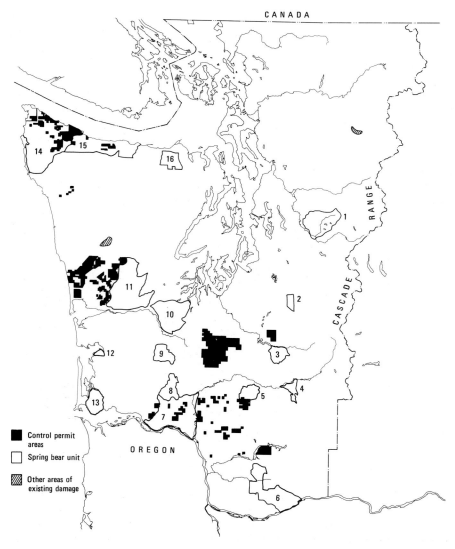

FIG. 13. - - Distribution of bear damage as of spring 1973.

26

The following summarization of the questionnaire returns are presented under headings which are condensed forms of questions three through twelve.

**Presence or Absence of Bear Damage**

Fifty-two questionnaires reported that bear damage was present and 20 reported that damage was absent. Of the latter, 18 were confident that damage did not exist in the area reported.

Bear damage was found to be widely distributed throughout western Washington. Damage resulting in frequent timber losses was reported in the northern, western, and southern portions of the Olympic Peninsula. Bear damage was shown to be common in the Cascade Mountains from Stampede Pass, in the southeast corner of King County, south to the Columbia River. In the Cascades damage extends from the upper tree zone to lower slopes on the west side and to the edge of the pure Ponderosa pine (*Pinus ponderosa*) stands on lower slopes of the east side. Damage is sporadic in upper altitudes and on the east slope of the Cascades, although significant damage does occur in localized areas. Damage is common throughout younger coniferous stands of low and intermediate elevations on the west slope of the Cascades, from Mount Rainier south to the Yacolt Burn in Clark and Skamania counties.

Areas where bear damage was absent or negligible are of special interest. Damage was sporadic along the east slope of the Olympic Peninsula and adjacent Kitsap Peninsula. On the Kitsap Peninsula, where gravelly soils and slow timber growth prevail, damage has been observed mainly to the trees growing along streams or adjacent to lakes. Damage was also negligible in the Black Hills, an area of susceptible second-growth conifers extending westward from the southern tip of Puget Sound. Although damage was heavy north of Chehalis River on the Olympic Peninsula, it was not reported on the major portion of the Willapa Hills which lie south of the Chehalis River.

A near total absence of damage was reported from the northern section of western Washington east of Puget Sound. Only two small areas of damage were reported from the area north of Stampede Pass, one near Skykomish in northern King County and one near Darrington in northern Snohomish County.

Damage was not observed in the lowland forests of the urban and agricultural area east of lower Puget Sound, and was seldom encountered in the lowland basin extending southward from Puget Sound to the Columbia River.

The eastern slope of the Cascade Mountains north of Stampede Pass was not included in the survey, but damage is known to occur in northern portions of Okanogan, Stevens and Pend Oreille counties.

**Evidence of Bear in Non-Damage Areas**

Black bear were known to be present in the area covered by 18 of the 20 questionnaires which reported no bear damage. Fifteen of these indicated that bear or bear signs were occasionally or commonly observed. Whatcom and Skagit counties were reported to have increasing bear populations. A high population of black bear was reported in the Elochoman River drainage of

Wahkiakum County. The San Juan Islands, as a group, were the only forest areas where bear were not observed.

## Predominant Timber Size in Reported Areas

Predominant timber size reported by 70 questionnaires is shown in Table 2. Information is separated into the areas which reported "damage present" and those which reported "damage absent." These data indicate that the area surveyed included all timber sizes, and that pole-size timber, which appears to be more susceptible to damage, was well represented in non-damage areas.

TABLE 2.—Predominant timber size in reported areas.

| | Predominant timber size | |
|---|---|---|
| Timber size | Questionnaires showing damage present | Questionnaires showing damage absent |
| Pole (5 to 15 inches dbh) | 23 | 6 |
| Saw (over 15 inches dbh) | 15 | 7 |
| Mixed pole and saw | 12 | 7 |

## Tree Species Damaged by Black Bear

Fifty-two questionnaires listed from one to seven tree species as damaged. Seventeen different species were reported as damaged. These consisted of 11 native conifers, 1 exotic conifer (redwood), and 5 native hardwoods (Table 3).

TABLE 3.—Bear-damaged tree species reported by 52 questionnaires.

| Common name | Scientific name | Times reported |
|---|---|---|
| Douglas-fir | Pseudotsuga menziesii | 50 |
| Western hemlock | Tsuga heterophylla | 37 |
| Western redcedar | Thuja plicata | 31 |
| Silver fir | Abies amabilis | 22 |
| Sitka spruce | Picea sitchensis | 12 |
| Red alder | Alnus rubra | 7 |
| Noble fir | Abies procera | 5 |
| Grand fir | Abies grandis | 5 |
| Bigleaf maple | Acer macrophyllum | 4 |
| Alpine fir | Abies lasiocarpa | 3 |
| Lodgepole pine | Pinus contorta | 3 |
| Western white pine | Pinus monticola | 3 |
| Black cottonwood | Populus trichocarpa var. hastata | 2 |
| Engelmann spruce | Picea englemanni | 1 |
| Willow | Salix spp. | 1 |
| Bitter cherry | Prunus emarginata | 1 |
| Redwood | Sequoia sempervirens | 1 |
| Ponderosa pine[a] | Pinus ponderosa | . . |
| Western larch[a] | Larix occidentalis | . . |

[a]Damaged tree species noted during study but not reported on questionnaire.

## Preference of Black Bear for Certain Tree Species

Forty-six of 52 questionnaires indicated that black bear damage certain, apparently preferred, tree species. Each questionnaire listed one to four species in order of observed apparent preference (Table 4).

TABLE 4.—Preferred tree species and order of preference based on incidence of damage.

| Tree species | Number of times listed as preferred species, by order of preference | | | |
|---|---|---|---|---|
| | 1st | 2nd | 3rd | 4th |
| Douglas-fir | 37 | 4 | 1 | 0 |
| Western hemlock | 1 | 11 | 3 | 0 |
| Western redcedar | 2 | 6 | 4 | 0 |
| Silver fir | 3 | 6 | 0 | 0 |
| Sitka spruce | 0 | 4 | 0 | 1 |
| Lodgepole pine | 3 | 0 | 0 | 0 |
| Alpine fir | 2 | 0 | 0 | 0 |

As these data are based on observations from a wide variety of timber types and sizes, assignment of species preferences are imprecise. An analysis of the questionnaire and damage maps, however, suggests that there are different preferred species in different locations or forest types. Alpine fir is the preferred species at high elevations in the Cascades, lodgepole pine on the east slopes of the Cascades, silver fir on the upper slopes and ridge tops of the Olympic and Cascade Mountains and Douglas-fir at the low and intermediate elevations in western Washington.

Preference for some species appears to be altered by changes in the physical characteristics of the bark. For example, western redcedar, western hemlock and silver fir frequently continue to be damaged until they reach a large diameter, apparently because they retain a smooth, relatively thin bark. Douglas-fir, which rapidly develops a rough, thick bark, is primarily susceptible to damage while in the pole stage.

## Predominant Age Classes of Damaged Trees

Predominant age classes of damaged trees reported in 49 questionnaires are listed in Table 5. Age classes reported varied from 10 to 20-year age class to the 200 to 250-year age class. The 20 to 40-year group comprised 56.8 percent of all classes listed.

## Average Diameter at Breast Height (DBH) of Damaged Trees

Average dbh of damaged trees reported by each of 51 questionnaires ranged from 5 to 10 inches in young stands to 18 to 30 inches in saw timber stands. The combined average for all diameter classes in each report was 9 to 15.6 inches dbh. Size of trees damaged varied with the different species damaged and size of the stand present in different areas. Damage to trees up to 5 feet in diameter was reported.

TABLE 5.—Predominant age classes of damaged trees.

| Age class (Years) | Number of times listed |
|---|---|
| 10 to 20 | 3 |
| 15 to 25 | 2 |
| 15 to 30 | 1 |
| 15 to 35 | 1 |
| 10 to 30 | 1 |
| 10 to 40 | 2 |
| 20 to 40 | 29 |
| 20 to 50 | 1 |
| 20 to 60 | 2 |
| 30 to 50 | 1 |
| 40 to 60 | 3 |
| 60 to 80 | 3 |
| 80 to 100 | 1 |
| 200 to 250 | 1 |

### Damage Variation in Relation to Stocking Density

Thirty-five of 51 questionnaires reported that intensity of damage varied significantly with stand density. Each of these listed one or more stand densities in which damage was heaviest (Table 6).

### Damage Variation in Relation to Site Class

Twenty of 49 questionnaires reported damage intensity varied according to site class. Site class reflects categories by which forest land is classified based on its productivity with respect to Douglas-fir growth. Class I sites are the most productive; that is, they produce a mature, marketable log more quickly than lower quality sites. Class V is the least productive. Site class where damage was heaviest, in relation to site class where damage was absent or negligible, is shown in Table 7.

These data indicate that the heaviest damage occurs on better quality sites (Classes I, II and III). This table does not show, however, the relationships between site class and damage in different areas of the state. This relationship is shown more clearly in Table 8, which includes site data from different areas of Washington. The lower rate on Site I may result from the fact that fewer areas of this type are present.

### Historical Bear Damage

Twenty-four of 46 questionnaires indicated bear damage has been occurring for at least 40 years in some areas. Forty-two of 49 questionnaires, however, reported the majority of bear damage had occurred within the past 15 years.

30

**TABLE 6.—Damage variation in relation to stocking density.**

| Stocking class | | Number reporting heaviest damage |
|---|---|---|
| Poor | (10 to 39 per cent) | 23 |
| Poor to medium | (10 to 69 per cent) | 6 |
| Medium | (40 to 69 per cent) | 4 |
| Medium to well | (40 to 100 per cent) | 1 |
| Well | (70 to 100 per cent) | 1 |

**TABLE 7.—Damage variation in relation to site class.**

| Site class | Damage reported | |
|---|---|---|
| | Heaviest | Absent or negligible |
| I | 6 | 2 |
| II | 11 | 1 |
| III | 11 | 1 |
| IV | 3 | 10 |
| V | 0 | 11 |

**TABLE 8.—Damage variation on selected areas statewide in relation to site class.**

| Reported by | County | Damaged site class | |
|---|---|---|---|
| | | Heaviest | Negligible or absent |
| Scott Paper Company | Thurston | II | IV, V |
| Simpson Logging Co. | Thurston, Mason, Grays Harbor | I, II, III | IV, V |
| Shelton District, DNR[a] | Mason | II, III | IV, V |
| Vancouver District, DNR | Skamania, Clark, Cowlitz | II, III | I, IV, V |
| Port Angeles District, DNR | Clallam | I, II, III | IV, V |
| Port Orchard District, DNR | Mason, Kitsap | III[b] | IV, V |
| Mineral District, U.S.F.S.[c] | Lewis | III | IV, V |
| Canyon District, U.S.F.S. | Skamania | III | IV, V |
| Quinault District, U.S.F.S.[d] | Grays Harbor | II, III | IV |

[a]Washington State Department of Natural Resources.
[b]No Site Class I or II persent in area.
[c]Gifford Pinchot National Forest, U. S. Forest Service.
[d]Olympic National Forest, U. S. Forest Service.

## DAMAGE EFFECTS

As discussed previously, while most bear damage involves bark removal at the base of the tree, debarking in the upper bole is common. Some trees are completely girdled, causing a loss through death of the entire tree or the crown. Many more trees, however, are only partly girdled and continue to live. These injured trees comprise a high proportion of many valuable stands.

Although wounds are well-known sites of entry for decay organisms, little was known about deterioration (infection and subsequent decay) in bear-injured conifers of the Pacific Northwest prior to the Cooperative Black Bear Study. This information was necessary if foresters were to be able to accurately determine the impact of bear damage and implement the highest returns from affected timber stands. Prior to the Cooperative Black Bear Study knowledge was based on two studies of decay resulting from old bear injuries on immature and semi-mature Douglas-fir in western Washington. Both studies indicated that loss from decay was not very significant (Childs and Worthington 1955; Anderson 1966). Many foresters, however, feel that decay may be significant in Douglas-fir or other conifers in some areas.

Theoretically, bear injuries should affect conifer trees in the same manner as logging injuries which have been investigated quite extensively for western hemlock and Sitka spruce and to some extent for Douglas-fir, silver fir and grand fir. Logging wounds on these conifers were found infected by many species of fungi and incidence of infection was usually high. Incidence of infection, types of fungi and amounts of decay varied with tree species and geographical location. Some species of fungi caused more decay than others. Decay was greater in western hemlock than in Douglas-fir, but similar in western hemlock and Sitka spruce. The larger the wound, the more likely it resulted in decay. In western hemlock and Sitka spruce the volume of decay increased in proportion to increase in age and area of injury. Even minor decay in the lower bole was considered significant because most of the wood and volume is concentrated in this portion of the tree. Artificial removal of bark from 40 percent of the bole circumference did not impair diameter growth in Douglas-fir (Hunt and Krueger 1962; Foster and Foster 1951; Foster et al. 1954; Shea 1960, 1967; Wright et al. 1947; Wright and Isaac 1956).

Decay or rot in wood is caused by fungi. The process of decay occurs in various stages. In the earliest or incipient stage, the wood appears sound and the only evidence of infection is a slight or distinct color change in the wood. After the incipient stage the wood undergoes an increasingly noticeable process of gradual decay. All stages of decay occur within a column of discolored wood extending up and down the bole from the wound. This column is no larger than the tree was at time of injury. Incipient decay may extend anywhere from a few inches to many feet beyond actual decay in the vertical direction; horizontally it is usually limited to one or two inches beyond decay (Boyce 1961; Shigo and Larson 1969).

Wood decay fungi are segregated into white and brown rot groups on the basis of different chemical activity. Brown rot fungi break down cellulose but do not affect lignin. Most white rot fungi utilize lignin primarily, but some also destroy cellulose. Wood in the early stages of brown rot infection is not usable for pulpwood, or where strength is required. Wood in the early stages of white rot infection can be used for some purposes (Boyce 1961; Foster and Foster 1953).

An investigation was initiated in 1967 by project personnel to study fungus infection and deterioration in several species of conifers commonly injured by black bear. Four study areas in western Washington were selected in intermediate or well-stocked stands of medium to large second-growth conifers with a high incidence of old bear injuries. Three areas were in rapid growth, low elevation coastal sites— Wishkah River drainage, central Grays Harbor County; Wynoochee River drainage, northern Grays Harbor County; and Pysht River area, Clallam County. The fourth area was in a moderate growth, higher elevation, inland site near Vail, Thurston County. Elevations ranged from 500 to 1,500 feet above sea level. The stand in the Wishkah area was mainly Douglas-fir; the other areas contained Douglas-fir and associate conifers. These study areas enabled comparisons of fungus infection on several conifer species within the same stands, as well as from widely separated stands. A representative sample of trees was felled in each area, selecting those with the largest and oldest wounds. The total sample included 40 Douglas-fir, 17 Sitka spruce, 14 western hemlock, 4 western redcedar and 1 grand fir. The sample was not as large as desired, but was considered sufficient to study general infection patterns.

Most trees had internal columns of discolored wood, often containing decay, associated with the wounds. Data were collected to compare volume of discolored and decayed wood with gross volume of merchantable wood above stump height. Methods proposed by Foster (1958) were used. After felling, each tree was cut into standard 16-foot logs, plus an 8-foot log for any excess, up to a 6-inch top diameter. Measurements taken included diameter and bark thickness of the top and bottom of each log, length of discoloration and two right angle measurements across the geometrical center of the area of discoloration at each cross-section cut. Based on these measurements, Smalian's formula was used to compute the volumes of deteriorated and merchantable wood for each tree. Fungus cultures, prepared from samples of decayed or discolored wood, were analyzed by mycologists of the Forest Disease Laboratory, Beltsville Maryland, and Colorado State University. Other data collected were total tree height, percent of bole circumference debarked, location and age of wound, diameter and age of tree at time of injury and examination, degree of wound healing and presence of decayed and insect-infected wood. Results are summarized in Tables 9 and 10. Deterioration is based on the volume of discolored and decayed wood.

The average age of trees when felled ranged from 24.9 years in the Wishkah area to 43.5 years in the Pysht area. All trees had typical basal wounds which varied in height up to about 6 feet. Eight of these also had more extensive wounds further up the bole, and 16 had two or three wounds

**TABLE 9.—Information on bear-injured trees examined for fungus infection and deterioration.**

| Species and area | No. trees | Total height (feet) | Diameter at stump (inches) | Age (Years) | Gross volume (Cu. Ft.) |
|---|---|---|---|---|---|
| | | — Average, except for single tree — | | | |
| Douglas-fir | | | | | |
| Wishkah | 20 | 56.8 | 13.3 | 24.9 | 13.4 |
| Wynoochee | 10 | 58.9 | 15.3 | 29.0 | 27.1 |
| Pysht | 6 | 84.7 | 17.6 | 41.2 | 41.8 |
| Vail | 4 | 69.2 | 17.4 | 31.2 | 33.0 |
| Total | 40 | 62.8 | 14.9 | 29.0 | 23.0 |
| Sitka spruce | | | | | |
| Pysht | 17 | 94.0 | 24.2 | 44.2 | 94.3 |
| Western hemlock | | | | | |
| Wynoochee | 13 | 67.8 | 15.7 | 35.3 | 32.3 |
| Pysht | 1 | 78.0 | 10.8 | 46.0 | 11.4 |
| Total | 14 | 68.5 | 15.3 | 36.1 | 30.8 |
| Western redcedar | | | | | |
| Wynoochee | 2 | 56.5 | 18.5 | 38.0 | 26.8 |
| Vail | 2 | 63.0 | 19.6 | 36.5 | 39.6 |
| Total | 4 | 59.7 | 19.1 | 37.2 | 33.2 |
| Grand fir | | | | | |
| Vail | 1 | 73.0 | 14.8 | 38.0 | 24.9 |

inflicted in different years. Removal of bark around the bole ranged from 38 percent for a single grand fir to an average of 66.7 percent for Douglas-fir. In relation to time of examination, the youngest wounds were in the Vail area (average, 7.0 years), and the oldest in the Pysht area (average, 18.5 years). Areas of wounds were not determined because of extensive scar tissue development.

Seventy-four of the trees had internal discoloration or decay indicating fungus infection associated with bear injuries. One or more species of fungi were isolated from the discolored or decayed wood in 47 of these trees; cultures were unsuccessful or contaminated for the remainder. The latter are listed as "unknown" fungi in Table 10 because deterioration was similar to known fungus infections. The only trees with no deterioration were two Douglas-fir in the Wishkah area. Average amounts of deterioration were high for all conifers; 10.0 percent for western hemlock, 17.3 percent for the single grand fir, 17.8 percent for Douglas-fir, 19.0 percent for Sitka spruce and 46.7 percent for western redcedar. The major proportion of this deterioration,

34

however, appeared to be sound discolored wood in the early stages of fungus infection. Amount of decay, in general, seemed far less than the amount of discoloration. Estimates of decay recorded while dissecting infected trees are summarized in Table 11.

**TABLE 10.—Fungus infections and deterioration in bear damage trees.**

| Area and fungus infection | No. trees | Percent of bole girdled | Age of wound (Years) | Gross tree volume (Cu. Ft.) | Deterioration[a] Vertical extent (Feet) | Volume (Cu. Ft.) | Percent of gross volume |
|---|---|---|---|---|---|---|---|
| | | Average, except for single trees | | | | | |
| | | **Douglas-fir** | | | | | |
| Wishkah | | | | | | | |
| *Stereum sanguinolentum*[b] | 13 | 62.1 | 9.1 | 12.1 | 1.9 | 0.3 | 2.5 |
| *Ceratocystis piceae* | 2 | 85.0 | 10.0 | 13.0 | 4.2 | 0.7 | 5.4 |
| Unknown spp. | 3 | 45.0 | 10.3 | 19.1 | 3.2 | 0.2 | 1.0 |
| Area total | 18 | 61.8 | 9.4 | 13.3 | 2.4 | 0.3 | 2.3 |
| Wynoochee | | | | | | | |
| *Stereum sanguinolentum*[b] | 7 | 72.1 | 7.4 | 11.5 | 14.6 | 3.4 | 29.6 |
| *Fomes cajanderi* | 1 | 60.0 | 15.0 | 103.8 | 42.0 | 50.5 | 48.6 |
| *Ceratocystis piceae* | 1 | 85.0 | 6.0 | 15.1 | 2.1 | 0.2 | 1.4 |
| Unknown spp. | 1 | 75.0 | 19.0 | 72.1 | 39.5 | 17.9 | 24.8 |
| Area Total | 10 | 72.5 | 9.2 | 27.1 | 18.6 | 9.2 | 33.9 |
| Pysht | | | | | | | |
| *Trametes serialis* | 1 | 70.0 | 21.0 | 45.0 | 8.2 | 2.5 | 5.5 |
| *Polyporus schweinitzii*[b] | 1 | 50.0 | 21.0 | 29.9 | 9.0 | 0.7 | 2.3 |
| *Ceratocystis piceae* | 1 | 75.0 | 18.0 | 23.0 | 5.3 | 0.8 | 3.5 |
| Unknown spp. | 3 | 64.3 | 29.0 | 51.0 | 11.2 | 3.0 | 5.9 |
| Area Total | 6 | 64.6 | 24.5 | 41.8 | 9.3 | 2.2 | 5.3 |
| Vail | | | | | | | |
| *Stereum sanguinolentum* | 3 | 75.0 | 8.0 | 34.7 | 21.2 | 10.2 | 29.4 |
| Unknown spp. | 1 | 85.0 | 10.0 | 27.8 | 5.5 | 17.7 | 63.7 |
| Area Total | 4 | 77.5 | 8.5 | 33.0 | 17.3 | 12.1 | 36.7 |
| Total—All Areas | 38 | 66.7 | 11.6 | 23.5 | 9.3 | 4.2 | 17.8 |
| | | **Western Redcedar** | | | | | |
| Wynoochee | | | | | | | |
| Unidentified wood rot spp. | 1 | 75.0 | 11.0 | 22.4 | 24.0 | 14.2 | 63.3 |
| Unkown spp. | 1 | 65.0 | 9.0 | 31.1 | 35.0 | 24.7 | 79.4 |
| Area Total | 2 | 70.0 | 10.0 | 26.8 | 29.5 | 19.5 | 71.4 |
| Vail | | | | | | | |
| *Odontia bicolor* | 1 | 50.0 | 5.0 | 54.7 | 14.0 | 12.0 | 22.0 |
| Unknown spp. | 1 | 45.0 | 5.0 | 24.5 | 20.0 | 11.2 | 45.7 |
| Area Total | 2 | 47.5 | 5.0 | 39.6 | 17.0 | 11.6 | 23.8 |
| Total—Both Areas | 4 | 58.7 | 7.5 | 33.2 | 23.2 | 15.5 | 46.7 |

**TABLE 10.—Continued**

| Area and fungus infection | No. trees | Percent of bole girdled | Age of wound (Years) | Gross tree volume (Cu. Ft.) | Deterioration[a] Vertical extent (Feet) | Volume (Cu. Ft.) | Percent of gross volume |
|---|---|---|---|---|---|---|---|
| | | | Average, except for single trees | | | | |
| **Grand Fir** | | | | | | | |
| Vail | | | | | | | |
|   Unidentified wood rot spp. | 1 | 38.0 | 10.0 | 24.9 | 13.0 | 4.3 | 17.3 |
| **Sitka Spruce** | | | | | | | |
| Pysht | | | | | | | |
|   *Fomes annosus*[c] | 4 | 64.2 | 18.7 | 110.7 | 22.2 | 21.5 | 19.4 |
|   *Stereum sanguinolentum* | 2 | 64.0 | 13.5 | 70.8 | 13.7 | 18.3 | 25.4 |
|   *Fomes pinicola* | 1 | 50.0 | 16.0 | 131.0 | 70.0 | 91.1 | 69.5 |
|   *Polyporus schweinitzii* | 1 | 25.0 | 19.0 | 69.4 | 5.0 | 1.4 | 2.0 |
|   *Ceratocystis piceae* | 1 | 75.0 | 15.0 | 77.3 | 8.5 | 3.1 | 4.0 |
|   Unknown spp. | 8 | 52.2 | 16.9 | 92.7 | 17.5 | 10.8 | 11.7 |
|   Area Total | 17 | 56.0 | 16.9 | 94.3 | 20.0 | 17.9 | 19.0 |
| **Western Hemlock** | | | | | | | |
| Wynoochee | | | | | | | |
|   *Fomes annosus* | 4 | 42.5 | 7.0 | 22.5 | 14.5 | 3.2 | 14.2 |
|   Unknown spp. | 9 | 58.9 | 13.9 | 36.7 | 14.1 | 3.4 | 9.3 |
|   Area Total | 13 | 53.9 | 11.8 | 32.3 | 14.2 | 3.3 | 10.2 |
| Pysht | | | | | | | |
|   *Armillaria mellea* | 1 | 25.0 | 11.0 | 11.4 | 4.0 | 0.5 | 4.4 |
| Total—Both areas | 14 | 51.8 | 11.7 | 30.8 | 13.5 | 3.1 | 10.1 |

[a]Includes all phases of infection: incipient, intermediate and advanced stages of decay.
[b]*Ceratocystis piceae* in one tree.
[c]One tree also infected with unidentified wood rot fungus and *Ceratocystis piceae*.

These data indicate that decay was more prevalent in Sitka spruce and western hemlock than in Douglas-fir, which is known to possess some resistance to decay (Foster 1958; Shea 1961). Decay was absent in 60.5 percent of the infected Douglas-fir. Insect borings were observed in decayed wounds on 14 trees. Dampwood termites (*Zootermyosis angusticollis*) and carpenter ants (*Camponotus herculeanus*) were identified in some of these wounds.

**TABLE 11.—Decay estimates of selected bear damaged trees on four areas in western Washington.**

| Amount of Decay | Douglas fir | Sitka spruce | Western hemlock | Western redcedar | Grand fir |
|---|---|---|---|---|---|
| None | 23 | 0 | 3 | 1 | 1 |
| Light | 8 | 2 | 1 | 1 | |
| Moderate | 7 | 14 | 10 | 2 | |
| Heavy | 0 | 1 | | | |

Three Douglas-fir, three Sitka spruce and two western hemlock had basal wounds extending far up the trunk, or extensive wounds higher on the bole. These trees had significantly higher amounts of deterioration, an average of 36.0 percent, than most trees with typical basal wounds.

The fungi isolated from bear injuries included four white rot species — *Stereum sanguinolentum, Fomes annosus, Armillaria mellea* and *Odontia bicolor;* four brown rot species — *Fomes pinicola, Polyporus schweinitzii, Trametes serialis* and *Fomes cajanderi;* and *Ceratocystis piceae,* one of several species which cause blue stain in wood. All of these except for *F. cajanderi* and *C. piceae* were previously reported to cause decay in conifers of the Pacific Northwest. *Stereum sanguinolentum, F. annosus* and *F. pinicola* are three of the most important decay fungi in the region (Hunt and Krueger 1962; Foster and Foster 1951; Foster et al. 1954; Shea 1960, 1961; Wright and Isaac 1956). Although the strength of wood is not significantly reduced by blue stain fungi, the discoloration commonly develops in logs, lumber and other wood products until dry, causing reduction in grade (Boyce 1961).

## Douglas-fir

*Stereum sanguinolentum* was the most prevalent fungus in Douglas-fir in three of the study areas. It was present in 60.5 percent of the infected trees and caused 36.5 percent of the total deterioration. In the Pysht area, *S. sanguinolentum* was found in Sitka spruce but not in Douglas-fir. The average amount of deterioration for trees infected with this fungus was much lower in the Wishkah area than in the Wynoochee and Vail areas, 2.5 percent as compared to 29.6 and 29.4 percent, respectively. The Wishkah and Wynoochee areas were not far apart (17 miles) and the size and age of trees and wounds were similar. Only 8 out of 23 trees infected with *S. sanguinolentum* showed evidence of rot; discoloration was the main defect. Individual trees were infected with *T. serialis, P. schweinitzii* and *F. cajanderi,* but only the latter showed significant deterioration, 48.6 percent. All of these trees, however, had moderate butt rot. Four trees were infected with *C. piceae.* Deterioration was quite low and one contained butt rot, apparently from some wood rot fungus not isolated. Total deterioration was much lower in the Wishkah and Pysht areas than in the Wynoochee and Vail areas, 2.3 and 5.3 percent compared to 33.9 and 36.7 percent, respectively. The reason for these differences was not apparent. The most prevalent fungi found in logging wounds were *F. pinicola* and *S. sanguinolentum* (Hunt and Krueger 1962; Shea 1961, 1967).

## Sitka Spruce

*Fomes annosus* and *S. sanguinolentum* were the predominant fungi in Sitka spruce, causing 35.3 percent of the infections and 40.3 percent of the total deterioration. The average amount of deterioration was high for both fungi, 19.4 and 25.4 percent, and all of the trees had moderate butt rot. One tree was infected with *P. schweinitzii* but deterioration and rot were minor. Another individual tree, 115 feet tall, and infected with *F. pinicola* contained 69.5 percent deterioration and very extensive rot. The bole of this tree was heavily scarred up to 47 feet. Eight trees were infected with unidentified fungi. Average deterioration was 11.7 percent and all contained rot. *Fomes pinicola* was the most prevalent and destructive fungus found in logging wounds on Sitka spruce. *Fomes annosus* and *S. sanguinolentum* occurred less frequently (Shea 1960; Wright and Isaac 1956).

## Western Hemlock

*Fomes annosus* was the most common fungus in western hemlock. Found in 28.6 percent of the infected trees, it caused 29.5 percent of the total deterioration. Average deterioration for four infected trees was 14.2 percent, but only one contained moderate butt rot. One tree infected with *A. mellea* contained 4.4 percent deterioration, including butt rot. Nine trees were infected with unknown fungi; the average deterioration was 9.3 percent and 7 had considerable butt rot. *Fomes annosus* and *S. sanguinolentum* were the most common infections found in logging wounds (Hunt and Krueger 1962; Shea 1961; Wright and Isaac 1956).

## Western Redcedar and Grand Fir

Deterioration was exceptionally high in the four western redcedar, ranging from 22.0 to 79.4 percent. One was infected with an unidentified wood rot fungus and contained moderate butt rot. Another was infected with *O. bicolor,* but decay was absent. Two were infected with unknown fungi. One contained considerable butt rot and the other was starting to decay. The single grand fir was infected with an unidentified wood rot fungus. Deterioration was high, 17.3 percent, but decay was absent.

This study revealed that bear injuries on the five tree species examined were highly susceptible to invasion by wood-destroying fungi. Types of fungi and patterns of infection in Douglas-fir, Sitka spruce and western hemlock were similar to those reported in logging injuries. Although several types of fungi were associated with bear injuries, two predominated: *S. sanguinolentum* and *F. annosus*. Types of fungi varies between tree species, and apparently between different areas. Two fungus infections that were reported commonly in logging injuries were absent in bear injuries; *F. pinicola* in Douglas-fir and *S. sanguinolentum* in western hemlock. Little information was obtained on the species of fungi for western redcedar and grand fir.

Volumes of deterioration obtained represent only the amount of wood infected by fungi. These volumes indicated that a high proportion of wood in all tree species was infected by fungi but they were difficult to interpret in terms of degrade or loss of wood and obviously were not comparable with decay volumes between tree species. For example, deterioration volumes tend to imply that decay in Douglas-fir would be greater than in western hemlock and about the same as in Sitka spruce. The estimates of decay, however, indicated that the amount of decay was considerably higher in Sitka spruce and western hemlock than in Douglas-fir. These estimates of decay conformed, in general, with results of logging injury studies, all of which used decay as the basis of wood losses. Deterioration also varied significantly between individual trees and different areas. These variations were apparently related to differences in species of trees and fungi, the age, size and location of injuries, and location site factors.

Most of the wood classed as deterioration appeared to be sound but discolored by the early stage of fungus invasion. Properties and uses of this wood were beyond the scope of the study. Most of the fungi, including the white rot species, cause eventual decay. Therefore, some impairment in strength of discolored wood and an increase of decay with time could logically be expected. Decay in the butt or upper bole, however, was the most obvious deterioration. Results suggest that decay may be significant in western hemlock and Sitka spruce and western redcedar. Decay was not very significant in Douglas-fir, except on some trees in the Pysht area. Breakage of trees commonly results from decay associated with bear wounds. More information on amounts of decay is needed for all tree species injured by bears.

The study basically showed that fungus infection in trees is too complex to arrive at any simple determination of the economic impact of management aspects of deterioration from bear injuries. Furthermore, deterioration is a rather nebulous term because fungi affect trees in various ways and the wood is used for different purposes. The following quotation by Shea (1960) seems to be an appropriate definition: "Deterioration affects the yield from forest trees by lowering quality or reducing yield by complete destruction of woody fibers. The extent to which yield is affected is related to the product desired. Even small amounts of decayed or discolored wood can cause cull or degrade of lumber, whereas, the same amount of imperfection may have little influence on the yield of pulp. In all instances, however, the use to which wood is placed and its quality are influenced in some manner by deterioration."

## DAMAGE SURVEY TECHNIQUES

The primary difficulty in determining characteristics and severity of black bear damage is a lack of comparable data. When considering the significance of bear damage to second-growth conifers it is unfortunate that little effort has been made to obtain accurate data through standardized procedures. Some informal surveys were conducted following discovery of specific instances of bear damage. Data collection in these instances, however, was based on desires of individual surveyors, not on standardized procedures. Surveys were generally not continued on a periodic basis, thus, no information concerning damage trends was obtained. Most bear damage determinations were then, and are now, based on opinions of field personnel and not on scientific data collected under controlled, standardized conditions. This lack of reliable data has made a detailed analysis of bear damage difficult, if not impossible.

Discussions with managing foresters, forestry research workers and forestry professors concerning the problems of data collection, resulted in identification of two methods for collection of desired data.

1. Obtain data in conjunction with regular forest inventory cruises.
2. Establish specific transects for collection of data.

Data collected with these techniques should include:

1. Species—damaged and undamaged.
2. Diameter breast height (dbh)—4.5 feet above ground.
3. Age of damage—current year or previous years.
4. Degree of girdle—percent of bole circumference.
5. Damaged trees recorded as injured or killed.

Use of these techniques standardize bear-damage data and provide the managing forester with comprehensive information concerning bear damage. These data are vital when facts regarding damage characteristics and effects of varying degrees of bear damage are evaluated. Both techniques are designed to allow study of damage trends through periodic data collection.

## Bear-damage Inventory Technique

The inventory technique for collection of bear-damage data was field tested in a cutting unit in northern Grays Harbor County. Inventory crews of the West Tacoma Newsprint Company collected bear-damage information in conjunction with regular inventory cruises. Categories of bear-damage information collected are shown in Figure 14.

1. Age of damage:
   Damage sustained in previous years — Class A
   Damage sustained in current year — Class B
2. Degree of girdle:
   **Percent trunk circumference**
       0 - 25                          Class 1
     26 - 50                        Class 2
     51 - 75                        Class 3
     76 - 100                     Class 4
3. Dead trees are recorded as — Class D

FIG. 14.—Data categories for bear damage inventory.

The following data are based on 799 prism plots (basal area factor: 25) and consist only of those plots showing bear damage. In actual operational use, data would be analyzed on the basis of the entire cutting unit. These data have been selected to illustrate characteristics of actual bear damage, and are not representative of damage in the area inventoried.

This section primarily shows what information should be collected by persons interested in evaluating bear damage and secondarily illustrates bear-damage characteristics in the field test area.

Species composition by dbh class and percent of each species in a particular class for plots showing bear damage in the field test area are shown in Table 12. As shown, western hemlock is the predominant species. A majority of the trees are over 11 inches dbh with the 11 to 15 inch dbh class encompassing the greater number of trees within the stand. These data describe the

40

stand as a whole, and when considered by species, the status of each species within the stand.

TABLE 12.—Tree species composition of bear damage area—Grays Harbor County, Washington.

| Species | Percent stand composition by DBH class | | | | | |
| | 5-10" | 11-15" | 16-20" | 21-25" | Over 25" | Combined |
|---|---|---|---|---|---|---|
| Douglas-fir | 8 | 20 | 41 | 37 | 17 | 22 |
| Hemlock | 67 | 63 | 50 | 58 | 69 | 61 |
| Cedar | 13 | 5 | 2 | 1 | 1 | 7 |
| Spruce | 1 | 1 | 2 | 2 | 10 | 2 |
| Red alder | 11 | 10 | 5 | 1 | 2 | 8 |
| Big leaf maple | * | * | 0 | 0 | 0 | * |
| White fir | * | * | * | * | 0 | * |
| Black cottonwood | 0 | 0 | * | 0 | 0 | * |
| Combined | 31 | 38 | 20 | 7 | 4 | |

*Less than 1 percent.

Incidences of bear damage, recorded by percent of species within each dbh class injured or killed, is shown in Table 13.

TABLE 13.—Percentage of trees in bear damage area injured and killed by species and DBH class—Grays Harbor County, Washington.

| Species | Percent injured/killed by DBH class | | | | | |
| | 5-10" | 11-15" | 16-20" | 21-25" | Over 25" | Combined |
|---|---|---|---|---|---|---|
| Douglas-fir | 6/5 | 12/9 | 20/5 | 23/3 | 7/7 | 16/6 |
| Hemlock | 4/1 | 16/2 | 19/1 | 9/1 | 2/0 | 12/1 |
| Cedar | 21/2 | 54/3 | 57/0 | 25/0 | 0/0 | 34/2 |
| Combined | 14/13 | 47/53 | 30/26 | 8/6 | 1/2 | 14/3 |

Western redcedar shows the highest percent of species injury and Douglas-fir shows the greatest percent of species killed. Injured and killed combined in western hemlock amount to 13 percent of the species. For Douglas-fir the comparable figure is 22 percent. Percentage figures are somewhat misleading as is seen when damage to western hemlock and Douglas-fir are compared on the basis of numbers of trees damaged. Although Douglas-fir showed a higher percent of species damage, a total of 192 damaged trees were recorded as opposed to 313 damaged western hemlock. Tabulation of data on the basis of percent of each species within each dbh class would show the damage picture of the stand as a whole rather than the status of each species in the stand as shown here.

A record of the degree of girdling in bear damage areas is essential to an evaluation of damage. Percent of bole circumference girdled is used in this evaluation. Table 14 shows percent of girdle by species and dbh class in the Grays Harbor cutting unit. A majority of Douglas-fir and western hemlock damage involved less than 25 percent girdling. Most of the western redcedar damage involved 51 to 75 percent girdling. The largest percent of damage to Douglas-fir was found in the 16 to 20 inch dbh class. The majority of damage to western hemlock and western redcedar was in the 11 to 15 inch dbh class.

TABLE 14.—Percent of girdle by tree species and dbh in bear damage area—Grays Harbor County, Washington.

| Species | DBH | Percent damaged by percent girdled | | | | Total injured | % species damage |
|---|---|---|---|---|---|---|---|
| | | 0-25 | 26-50 | 51-75 | 76-100 | | |
| Douglas-fir | 5-10" | 0[a] | 67 | 0 | 33 | 6 | 4 |
| | 11-15" | 45 | 37 | 13 | 5 | 38 | 28 |
| | 16-20" | 46 | 28 | 18 | 8 | 67 | 49 |
| | 21-25" | 48 | 26 | 17 | 9 | 23 | 17 |
| | Over 25" | 0 | 50 | 50 | 0 | 2 | 2 |
| | | 44[b] | 32[b] | 16[b] | 8[b] | 136 | 27[c] |
| Hemlock | 5-10" | 44 | 38 | 9 | 9 | 34 | 12 |
| | 11-15" | 50 | 28 | 17 | 5 | 155 | 55 |
| | 16-20" | 49 | 32 | 18 | 1 | 76 | 27 |
| | 21-25" | 44 | 50 | 6 | 0 | 16 | 6 |
| | Over 25" | 50 | 50 | 0 | 0 | 2 | * |
| | | 49[b] | 31[b] | 16[b] | 4[b] | 283 | 56[c] |
| Cedar | 5-10" | 24 | 30 | 30 | 16 | 33 | 38 |
| | 11-15" | 16 | 33 | 40 | 11 | 43 | 49 |
| | 16-20" | 10 | 20 | 50 | 20 | 10 | 12 |
| | 21-25" | 0 | 100 | 0 | 0 | 1 | 1 |
| | Over 25" | 0 | 0 | 0 | 0 | 0 | 0 |
| | | 18[b] | 31[b] | 37[b] | 14[b] | 87 | 17[c] |
| % of Total girdling | | 42 | 32 | 20 | 6 | | |

[a]Percent of total damage present within DBH class.
[b]Percent of total damage present within girdling range indicated.
[c]Percent of total damage present.
*Less than 1 percent.

Damage trends shown in Table 15 reveal that western redcedar and western hemlock were being damaged at a faster rate than Douglas-fir.

**Bear-damage Transect Technique**

The purpose of forest inventory cruises dictates that they be representative of large areas, and since bear damage is often localized, it is possible that the regular inventory cruise will not give the desired coverage for localized

42

TABLE 15.—Age of damage in bear damage area—Grays Harbor County, Washington

| Species | % Current year damage | % Old damage |
|---|---|---|
| Douglas-fir | 2 | 98 |
| Western hemlock | 14 | 86 |
| Western redcedar | 20 | 80 |
| % Total damage | 12 | 88 |

damage hot-spots. Establishment of specific bear-damage transects will supply this information. Specific areas of damage can be analyzed and evaluated over a period of years by means of bear-damage transects. These transects should be permanently located to allow subsequent measurement and documentation of damage trends.

Since these transects will be established in localized areas of bear damage, specific information regarding the site should be recorded. Site information, in conjunction with damage data, is useful in determining relationships between timber sites and bear damage. Desired site information is shown in Figure 15.

1. Location.
2. Soil type.
3. Forest type and dominant understory.
4. Stand age and stocking class.
5. Land use and fire history.

FIG. 15.—Bear damage transect site information.

Bear damage data collected are similar to those collected in conjunction with the forest inventory cruise (Fig. 16). Formats of transect site description and damage data forms are in Appendix D.

1. Total trees within transect by species and dbh.
2. Injured trees within transect by species and dbh.
3. Dead trees within transect by species and dbh.
4. Age of damage recorded as current year or previous years.
5. Degree of girdle recorded as 0-25, 26-50, 51-75, or 76-100 percent of bole circumference.

FIG. 16.—Bear damage transect data categories.

Field tests of black bear damage transects were conducted by U. S. Forest Service and project personnel. Various sizes and types of plots were measured and evaluated from the standpoint of data collection and for ease and practicability of remeasurement. Circular plots were tested but were difficult to relocate for subsequent remeasurement. Belt, or strip transects were generally found to be best suited for collection of damage data and subsequent remeasurement. Although not used during this study, circular plots may be used when necessary. Special care must be taken, however, to insure accurate relocation of plots. Transect width and length, or plot size, can be determined by the stocking class and size of the area to be sampled. Recommended transect widths are shown in Figure 17. Transect length is determined by the size of the area sampled and percent coverage desired.

| Stand | Transect width | Area sampled per chain of transect length (66 feet) |
|---|---|---|
| Heavily Stocked | 6.6 feet | .01 acre |
| Medium Stocked | 33.6 feet | .05 acre |
| Open Stand | 66.0 feet | .10 acre |

FIG. 17.—**Recommended bear damage transect widths and area sampled per chain of transect length.**

The beginning point of the transect is marked with a permanent, numbered, iron post adequately described for subsequent relocation. Each chain of transect length is also permanently marked. Injured and dead trees within the transect are sprayed with colored paint for identification. Red is recommended for dead trees and blue for injured trees. If it is desirable to follow the fate of individual injured trees to determine deterioration and mortality, trees can be tagged with metal numbered tags for identification.

Use of inventory and transect techniques must be stressed for any evaluation of bear damage. Accurate data regarding damage in an area are needed before the forest manager can make any valid evaluation of that damage. In too many cases damage is assessed on opinion rather than fact.

Studies presently underway will allow determination of the economic effects of varying degrees of damage. Data obtained from inventories and transects, when analyzed in light of these studies, will provide an economic evaluation of bear damage that has been impossible up to this time. Knowledge of the economic effects of bear damage will be important in forest management, but if damage characteristics of the stand are not known, the new technique will be useless.

Inventory and transect data regarding bear damage are important to the forest manager if he is to insure that recommended control programs are economically sound. This is equally true for the wildlife manager who must limit control operations to those areas with substantiated damage.

## TREE SPECIES PREFERENCES OF BLACK BEAR

In responses to the damage questionnaire discussed previously, one significant aspect of black bear damage was apparent: Black bear will damage certain tree species in apparent preference over other species in the same stand. Preference for sapwood of certain species appears to vary with geographical area and forest type. Alpine fir is reported to be the preferred species at high elevations in the Cascade Mountains, silver fir is preferred on upper slopes and ridge tops in the Olympic and Cascade Mountains, and lodgepole pine is preferred on east slopes of the Cascade Mountains. Douglas-fir is the preferred species at low and intermediate elevations of western Washington. This apparent preference for certain coniferous species was identified as an important aspect of any investigation.

44

Forest survey and bear-damage data were obtained from West Tacoma Newsprint Company to determine preference ratings for various species in the Damage Study Area in Grays Harbor County. Collected data were from 2177 prism plots of various sizes (total area not determined) measured during 1962 and 1963.

Coniferous species composition of the inventoried area is shown in Table 16. Alder was recorded during the inventory, but is not included. Of 2488 alders tallied during the inventory, none had sustained bear damage. As shown, Douglas-fir is the dominant species in the 2 to 11 inch dbh class, with western hemlock dominant in dbh classes over 12 inches and overall within the area. Western redcedar and Sitka spruce are relatively minor species.

TABLE 16.—Coniferous species composition of bear damage area—Grays Harbor County, Washington.

| Species | Percent damaged by DBH class | | | % of area |
| | 2-5" | 6-11" | Over 12" | |
|---|---|---|---|---|
| Douglas-fir | 49 | 47 | 37 | 40 |
| Western hemlock | 44 | 45 | 54 | 51 |
| Western redcedar | 4 | 4 | 4 | 4 |
| Sitka spruce | 3 | 4 | 5 | 5 |
| % of area | 7 | 28 | 65 | |

Bear damage, both injured and killed, is shown in Table 17 by species and dbh class. Thirty-four percent of the Douglas-fir present on the area were damaged. This constituted 67 percent of the Douglas-fir present. Twenty-three percent of all trees over 12 inches dbh were damaged. These constituted 72 percent of the total damage present. Twenty-one percent of all coniferous trees in the area were damaged.

By combining portions of Tables 16 and 17, species composition in the damage area can be compared with damage sustained by species within each dbh class. Data in Table 18 show that Douglas-fir, while constituting only 40 percent of the area inventory, accounts for 67 percent of total damage. Western hemlock, the most commonly represented species at 51 percent, accounts for only 30 percent of the damage.

Data discussed this far indicates a definite preference for Douglas-fir in the area inventoried. Variance in species availability and damage sustained, however, make it difficult to ascribe definite preference ratings.

## Determination of Preference Ratings

Stand composition or availability of different coniferous species varies. These variations must be accounted for in any valid preference determination.

This can be accomplished by equating species availability to a constant, and calculating the projected damage at the hypothetical constant.

$$\frac{\text{Percent Availability}}{\text{Percent Damage}} = \frac{\text{Constant (100)}}{\text{Damage Constant (DK)}}$$

Calculation of the above expression, solving for the Damage Constant (DK), will provide a damage figure which is not influenced by the effects of availability acting in conjunction with pure chance.

TABLE 17.—Bear damage[a] in bear damage area—Grays Harbor County, Washington

| | DBH class | | | |
|---|---|---|---|---|
| | 2-5" | 6-11" | Over 12" | |
| Species | % Damaged by Species/Class | % Damaged by Species/Class | % Damaged by Species/Class | % Total damage Species/Area |
| Douglas-fir | 7/82 | 30/73 | 40/65 | 34/67 |
| Western hemlock | 1/14 | 11/26 | 14/32 | 12/30 |
| Western redcedar | 0/0 | 4/1 | 13/2 | 9/2 |
| Sitka spruce | 7/4 | 1/* | 3/1 | 3/1 |
| Area totals | 4/2 | 19/26 | 23/72 | 21/100 |

*Less than 1 percent.
[a]Both injured and killed trees.

TABLE 18.—Species composition compared to total damage in bear damage area— Grays Harbor County, Washington.

| | DBH class | | | |
|---|---|---|---|---|
| | 2-5" | 6-11" | Over 12" | |
| Species | % Class/Damage | % Class/Damage | % Class/Damage | Total % of Area/Damage |
| Douglas-fir | 49/82[a] | 47/73 | 37/65 | 40/67[b] |
| Western hemlock | 44/14 | 45/26 | 54/32 | 51/30 |
| Western redcedar | 4/0 | 4/1 | 4/2 | 4/2 |
| Sitka spruce | 3/4 | 4/* | 5/1 | 5/1 |
| Area totals | 7/2 | 28/26 | 65/72 | 100/21[c] |

*Less than 1 percent.
[a]Species composition/damage within dbh class.
[b]Species composition/damage within stand.
[c]% of total stand damaged.

To determine preference ratings between species, the Damage Constants of the species involved are compared to a base species. In this area the base species is Douglas-fir, the apparent preferred species.

$$\frac{\text{DK of Compared Species}}{\text{DK of Base Species}} \ \text{X} \ 100 \ = \ \text{Preference Rating}$$

Preference ratings of conifers in the Damage Study Area are shown in Table 19. Data in the combined rating column show that if 100 percent of the Douglas-fir were damaged, you would find 35 percent of the western hemlock damaged, 30 percent of the western redcedar damaged, and 12 percent of the Sitka spruce damaged. When differences in probability of damage between dbh classes are evaluated, it appears that western hemlock is more apt to be damaged in the 6 to 11 inch dbh class. Damage to western redcedar is most prevalent in the over 12 inch dbh class. Damage to Sitka spruce appears to be insignificant except in the 2 to 5 inch dbh class. Douglas-fir with a DK of 167 in the 2 to 5 inch dbh class, 155 in the 6 to 11 inch dbh class and 176 in the over 12 inch dbh class, is more susceptible to damage when over 12 inch dbh.

**TABLE 19.**—**Coniferous species preference ratings, damage study area—Grays Harbor County, Washington**

| Species | Preference rating by DBH class | | | Area preference rating |
|---|---|---|---|---|
| | 2-5″ | 6-11″ | Over 12″ | |
| Douglas-fir | 100 | 100 | 100 | 100 |
| Western hemlock | 19 | 37 | 34 | 35 |
| Western redcedar | 0 | 16 | 28 | 30 |
| Sitka spruce | 80 | 0 | 11 | 12 |

Additional species preference data were obtained from nine transects measured in three geographical areas of western Washington. Line transects one-half chain wide and 20 chains long were used. Where required by damage characteristics or topography, transects were broken into 5 or 10 chain lengths until 20 chains of damage could be measured.

General areas where different species were reported as preferred were selected based upon results of the bear damage questionnaire. The cooperating agency was contacted and areas of heavy bear damage selected for transect locations. The general direction or long axis of the damage pattern determined the transect azimuth.

Damage was recorded for 12 coniferous and two hardwood species present on the areas (Table 20). Data indicate that Douglas-fir, with few exceptions, is the preferred species in low elevation forests of western Washington. Noble fir, Engelmann spruce and silver fir are generally preferred species in the Cascade Mountains of eastern Lewis County. Lodgepole pine and western white pine are preferred species in the Cascades south of Mount Adams.

TABLE 20.—Preference ratings of different tree species in three geographical areas of western Washington[a].

| | General transect location | | | | | | | | |
|---|---|---|---|---|---|---|---|---|---|
| | Grays Harbor County | | Eastern Lewis County | | | | South of Mt. Adams | | |
| Transect No. | 1 | 2 | 3 | 4 | 5 | 6 | 7 | 8 | 9 |
| **Species** | | | | | | | | | |
| Douglas-fir | 100[b] | 100 | 100 | . . . | 100 | . . . | . . . | . . . | 20 |
| Western hemlock | 2 | 59 | 47 | . . . | 0[c] | . . . | . . . | . . . | 0 |
| Western redcedar | . . . | 157[b] | 107 | . . . | . . . | . . . | . . . | . . . | 0 |
| Sitka spruce | . . . | 0 | . . . | . . . | . . . | . . . | . . . | . . . | . . . |
| Red alder | . . . | . . . | 34 | . . . | . . . | . . . | . . . | . . . | . . . |
| Black cottonwood | . . . | . . . | 155[b] | . . . | . . . | . . . | . . . | . . . | 0 |
| Vine maple | . . . | . . . | 0 | . . . | . . . | . . . | . . . | . . . | . . . |
| Bitter cherry | . . . | . . . | 0 | . . . | . . . | . . . | . . . | . . . | . . . |
| Silver fir | . . . | . . . | . . . | 100 | 21 | 100 | . . . | . . . | . . . |
| Mountain hemlock | . . . | . . . | . . . | 44 | . . . | 115 | . . . | . . . | 0 |
| Engelmann spruce | . . . | . . . | . . . | . . . | 156[b] | . . . | . . . | . . . | 51 |
| Noble fir | . . . | . . . | . . . | . . . | . . . | 158[b] | . . . | . . . | . . . |
| Grand fir | . . . | . . . | . . . | . . . | . . . | 0 | . . . | . . . | . . . |
| Lodgepole pine | . . . | . . . | . . . | . . . | . . . | . . . | 100[b] | 100[b] | 23 |
| Ponderosa pine | . . . | . . . | . . . | . . . | . . . | . . . | 0 | 0 | . . . |
| White fir | . . . | . . . | . . . | . . . | . . . | . . . | 0 | 0 | 29 |
| Western white pine | . . . | . . . | . . . | . . . | . . . | . . . | . . . | . . . | 100[b] |
| Western larch | . . . | . . . | . . . | . . . | . . . | . . . | . . . | . . . | 80 |

[a]Douglas-fir was used as the base species in determination of preference ratings.
[b]Preferred species on transect.
[c]Preference rating of 0 indicates species present but not damaged.

Although occurring in three of seven transects in the Cascade Mountains, Douglas-fir was not the preferred species in that area. Western redcedar was the preferred species in one transect in Grays Harbor County, and in one transect in eastern Lewis County.

Specific location of the nine transects, stand composition by species, bear damage by species and dbh, damage and dbh class comparisons and preference rating tables are provided in Appendix B.

## BEAR DAMAGE CONTROL

Damage to coniferous species by black bear may affect the ultimate species composition of forests and their wood fiber yield. Forestland managers are increasingly aware of all detrimental influences on forest growth as the ever-increasing demand for wood products continues. Forestland managers go to great effort to protect their tree crops from fire, insects and disease. Similar efforts may be necessary to protect this crop from predation by animals.

As with all damaging influences on a forest, a certain amount can be sustained before it is economically feasible to prevent it from occurring. Such is the case with bear damage. In the early 1950's, the Society of American Foresters, a professional group, trained in the science and practice of forestry,

Plate I: Douglas-fir killed by black bear in southwest Washington, 1 year following damage.

**Plate II:** Douglas-fir killed by black bear showing basal wound.

**Plate III:** Red flagging showing bear damaged Douglas-fir in a tree plantation near the North Fork Snoqualmie River in Washington.

Plate IV: Red flagging on Weyerhaeuser tree farm, 1 year after damage.

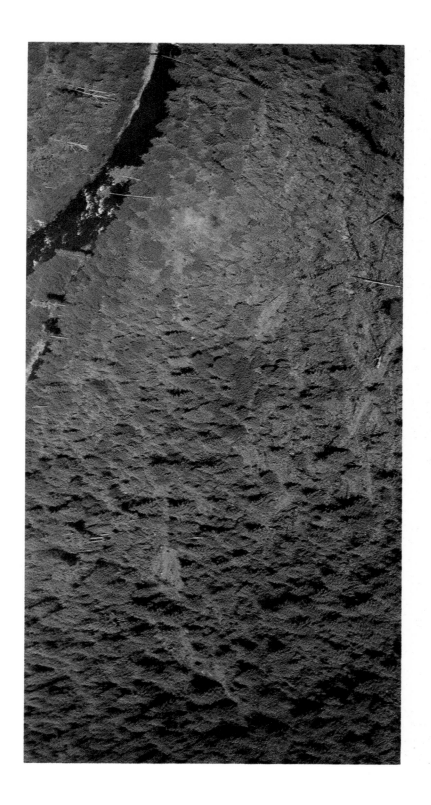

Plate V: Bear damage on Spring Bear Unit 14, Huffaker Mountain (see Fig. 13).

**Plate VI:** Bear damage to Douglas-fir on a Weyerhaeuser tree farm in Washington.

**Plate VII:** Bear damage to western redcedar in Clallam County, Washington.

**Plate VIII:** Basal damage showing tooth pattern in sapwood following damage by black bear.

became increasingly aware of the damage being done by black bear to second growth forests which abounded following the earlier day timber harvest on the Olympic Peninsula. As mentioned earlier, this concern culminated in the black bear being declared a predator in five counties on the Olympic Peninsula. Hunting, without license or bag limit, was permitted on a year-round basis. The liberal hunting policy was adopted in anticipation that sufficient hunting pressure would be achieved to reduce the bear population to a level where black bear and trees could again live in harmony.

During the 1950's several forestland owners retained the services of a Federal wildlife control agent and professional hunters to trap and hunt bear on a wide-spread basis throughout the counties where damage was occurring.

In 1960 the Washington Forest Protection Association (WFPA), a trade association of private and municipal forestland owners, (Appendix C), organized a cooperative effort in the Grays Harbor area to meet this problem. The organizational theory was that since bear damage was widespread and affecting many landowners, it would be more efficient to unify hunting efforts of individual landowners and distribute the costs of the operation on a proportional basis based upon respective acreages of ownership.

Similar cooperative efforts were organized in the northern portion of the Olympic Peninsula and southwest Washington in 1961. In 1967, a similar effort was organized in the central area in the vicinity of Chehalis. In 1971 a serious bear damage problem developed on the North Fork of the Snoqualmie River near North Bend. An additional part-time hunter was hired by WFPA in 1972 to handle this area. This is the most northerly area where bear damage control programs have been conducted. There is, however, significant bear damage occurring on 20-year-old Douglas-fir plantations on U.S. Forest Service lands along the south fork of the Suiattle River near Darrington.

In 1972 the various local cooperative programs and individual professional hunters were consolidated into a single program called the WFPA Animal Damage Control Service.

During the early years of control, steel traps and hound hunting were used exclusively. A WFPA hunter, Jack Aldrich, developed the Aldrich Spring Activated Animal Snare which completely replaced the use of steel bear traps. This cable spring device revolutionized control operation because the snare was light, inexpensive and completely harmless to humans (Fig. 18A). The device operates on the principle that when a bear steps on the snare's trigger, a 3/16 inch cable loop is thrown over the bear's foot and held secure. In 1968 the WFPA developed a miniature radio transmitter for installation with the snares. When a snare is sprung, it turns on the transmitter which emits a pulsating signal which is monitored by the hunter using a special radio receiver as he drives around his snare line (Fig. 18B). This innovation permits the hunter to place snares in what was heretofore inaccessible areas since one transmitter model has a range of two miles. Practically all snares used in the program today are so equipped.

As a result of information gained in the Cooperative Black Bear Study, policies of the control program have been modified to capitalize on any information which improves the effectiveness and efficiency of control operations.

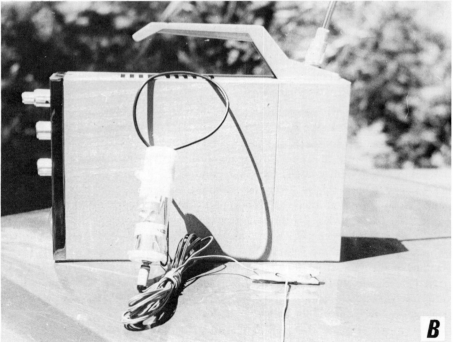

FIG. 18.—Aldrich spring activated foot snare (A) and radio signal device (B).

50

The most significant change was restricting professional hunters to damage areas only. Radio-tracking data showed that a given bear normally returns to the same general area each spring. Thus, the probability of catching bear causing tree damage is greatly increased if bears are taken only from damage areas. As a result, hunting was restricted to much smaller geographical areas and the control kill was reduced from approximately 500 bear per year to less than 250 per year.

Hunters are paid a fixed monthly salary plus expenses by WFPA. Control operations are conducted in specific areas for which the Washington State Game Department has issued special bear damage control permits. Bonuses for the number of bear taken have been long discarded since learning that the total number of bear taken has little influence on the incidence of bear damage. The objective of WFPA's control program is to minimize bear damage consistent with cost and values protected rather than killing bears. Hunters are employed for a period of 3 to 8 months each year. At one time there were eight professional hunters employed by the WFPA; however, at the present time there are four hunters located in the Forks, Aberdeen, Chehalis and Longview areas. Control methods generally consist of setting foot snares in damage areas. Cheese manufacturing derivatives or beef heads are used for bait.

In 1969 the black bear was classified as a game animal throughout the state. The WFPA supported this classification. It was felt this would enable manipulation of sport bear hunting seasons in the future to allow more effective use of the sports hunter in solving bear damage problems. In 1973 a special spring bear season incorporating this concept was set by the Washington State Game Commission. Ths special season was established in 16 bear damage areas during the months of April, May and June. This required sportsmen wanting to hunt bear in the spring to do so only in a bear damage area. Snaring operations in the special areas were suspended during the spring season, allowing unrestricted effort by hound hunters who have avoided control areas in the past because of the fear that their hounds might be snared. A more complete discussion of this season is given in the Management Section.

What the economic impact of bear damage is, is a question that has never been satisfactorily answered. A forestland owner who sees thousands of trees die as a result of bear damage knows that it is a significant problem which requires corrective action. The less dramatic damage where fewer trees are killed over longer periods of time, however, is difficult to assess. Even more difficult are intelligent decisions regarding the need for control operations. In 1971 the WFPA contracted with the Institute of Forest Products, College of Forest Resources, University of Washington to design a method by which forestland owners could reliably assess the economic significance of bear damage. The field data needed to substantiate the formulas developed for this purpose require two successive years of aerial photography. Results of this study will not be available until 1974.

Forestland owners recognize that the bear damage control program is a highly sensitive activity in this day of environmental awareness. The WFPA conducts the program in the most responsible manner possible and is always willing to discuss the program with interested persons. As long as tree farming remains the backbone of Washington's state economy, and repeated tree crops are being cultured, occasional damage by black bear will be a problem. Hopefully, the taking of problem animals by sportsmen can be maximized and the need to use professional hunters minimized. There will, however, probably always remain a need to take some bear with professional damage control personnel.

# HABITAT

To further document characteristics of the habitat which black bear occupied, two investigations concerned with vegetation were conducted. One was concerned with vegetative composition of black bear habitat, primarily food species, and the other with chemical analysis of the sapwood in species found damaged by black bear. Discussion of correlations and inter-relationships between sapwood constituents, food preferences and vegetative composition will be presented in the Natural History Section, together with data concerning the food habit studies. Results of the vegetation inventory and sapwood analysis follow.

## VEGETATION INVENTORY

A vegetation inventory was conducted in the non-damage and damage study areas of Grays Harbor County. Areas of spring black bear activity were determined by examination of location data obtained during radio-tracking activities. Black bear habitat transects in the two study areas were based upon these known animal locations. Locations were plotted on aerial photographs to serve as the basis for establishing specific transects. Predetermined transect lines were adhered to as closely as possible to reduce sampling station selection bias. The 13-foot Browse Survey method was revised for collection of vegetation data.

Species recorded were selected on the basis of food habit studies which are discussed in the Natural History Section. Of particular interest were the key food species identified during the study: grasses (Graminae), false dandelion (*Hypochaeris radicata*), salmonberry (*Rubus spectabilis*), *Rubus* spp. (other than salmonberry), devil's club (*Oplopanax horridum*), skunk cabbage (*Lysichitum americanum*) and salal. Other forbs found were combined in a single category as were deciduous and coniferous trees. Only vegetation below five feet in height was measured. Plants below this height were considered generally accessible to black bear for selection as food items.

### Non-damage Area

Frequency of occurrence and canopy coverage of recorded species are shown in Table 21. Data were collected from 464 sampling stations. Key spring food items, mentioned above, represented a frequency of 23.5 percent and canopy coverage of 21.4 percent.

52

## Damage Area

There were 453 sampling stations measured in the damage study area. Frequency of occurrence and canopy coverage of measured species are shown in Table 21. Key spring black bear food species occurred 26.4 percent of the time and made up 24.4 percent of the canopy cover.

TABLE 21.—Species frequency and canopy coverage by percent—Spring vegetation transects on damage and non-damage study areas, Grays Harbor County, Washington[a]

| Species | Frequency | | Canopy coverage | |
|---|---|---|---|---|
| | Non-damage | Damage | Non-damage | Damage |
| **Key food species** | | | | |
| Grass | 5.5 | 2.5 | 2.3 | 2.2 |
| False dandelion | 0.6 | 1.5 | 0.2 | 0.8 |
| Salmonberry | 5.1 | 7.8 | 6.2 | 4.6 |
| Rubus spp.[b] | 10.5 | 8.3 | 7.1 | 4.6 |
| Salal | 8.4 | 14.0 | 9.3 | 15.9 |
| Skunk cabbage | 0.1 | 0.1 | 0.1 | 0.1 |
| Devil's club | 3.8 | 0.5 | 3.4 | 0.8 |
| **Other species** | | | | |
| Huckleberry | 7.9 | 7.5 | 5.8 | 3.9 |
| Cascara | 1.1 | 2.7 | 0.7 | 1.8 |
| Forbs | 17.6 | 16.7 | 17.1 | 14.8 |
| Deciduous | 5.8 | 5.3 | 4.5 | 4.4 |
| Coniferous | 4.8 | 6.9 | 4.5 | 8.8 |
| **Non-vegetative** | | | | |
| Litter | 24.8 | 21.1 | 36.9 | 31.9 |
| Rock | 0.5 | 0.5 | 0.2 | 0.7 |
| Bare ground | 3.5 | 4.6 | 1.7 | 4.7 |

[a]Only vegetation below 5 feet in height measured.
[b]All Rubus spp. except salmonberry.

## Comparison of Non-damage and Damage Areas

Data in Table 21 indicate there is little difference between the two study areas when key food species are compared. Key species occurred 23.5 percent of the time on non-damage transects and on 26.4 percent of the damage area. Key species represented 21.4 and 24.4 percent, respectively, of the habitat cover measured in the non-damage and damage areas. Differences between individual species appear to be of significance in some instances, particularly salmonberry, devil's club and salal.

Although salmonberry occurrs less frequently in the non-damage area, it constitutes a larger percent of the total vegetative cover. While these data cannot verify it, subjective field observations indicate that salmonberry in the damage area is being heavily utilized by other animals prior to the emergence of the black bear in the spring. This would account, at least in part, for the differences in the data, with more but smaller salmonberry bushes in the damage area.

## SAPWOOD ANALYSIS

Studies on the damage and non-damage study areas in Grays Harbor County indicated a descending order of preference for the principal damaged species as follows: Douglas-fir, western hemlock, western redcedar and red alder. Of the many tree characteristics which may have influenced this preference, chemical composition of the sapwood in the spring seemed a major factor. This section reports chemical analysis of sapwood tissue collected in May 1965 from the above four species growing on the damage and non-damage study areas. This study was conducted by personnel of the Forestry Sciences Laboratory, Pacific Northwest Forest and Range Experiment Station, Forest Service, U.S. Department of Agriculture, Olympia, Washington. Results have been previously published by M. A. Radwan, in Forest Science, Volume 15, Number 1, March 1969. Portions of the report are included to simplify later discussion with respect to bear damage.

### Tissue Sampling

Sapwood of each species from each of the two study areas served as test material. Only healthy trees of the 20 to 30-year-old class and approximately 10 to 12 inches dbh were used. Two composite sapwood samples, of approximately 400 grams each, were taken during the morning hours in May 1965 from each of the four species on both areas. Each sample was taken from 10 trees selected from approximately 5 acres of similar elevation, aspect, soil series and vegetation composition. Sample preparation and analytical methods used are covered in the referenced report.

### Results

Concentrations of the chemical constituents of sapwood, summarized in Table 22, are expressed on a fresh-weight basis to allow comparison of levels as the animal encounters them in feeding.

There were only slight variations in moisture content among species and none within species from the two study areas. Average moisture content for all samples was approximately 90 percent, indicating a low dry matter content of about 10 percent.

Ash content was lowest in Douglas-fir, intermediate in western hemlock and highest in western redcedar and red alder. Here again, there were no differences between the species from the two areas.

Mineral elements in the sapwood, as shown by the ash content, were low. They averaged less than 1 percent on a fresh-weight basis, and about 7 percent when expressed on a dry-weight basis. This indicates that an average of approximately 93 percent of the dry matter was organic in nature.

Concentrations of reducing, non-reducing and total sugars differed significantly among species. Within species, however, sapwood from the two areas contained similar amounts of the sugars.

Total sugar content was highest in Douglas-fir and to a lesser extent in western hemlock, medium in western redcedar and lowest in red alder. The

54

TABLE 22.—Concentration of selected chemical constituents in the fresh sapwood of four tree species in the spring[a].

| Species and collection area[b] | Moisture | Ash | Reducing sugars | Non-reducing sugars | Total sugars | N | P | Ca | Mg | Fe | Mn |
|---|---|---|---|---|---|---|---|---|---|---|---|
| | | | | | Percent | of Fresh Weight | | | | | |
| Douglas-fir | | | | | | | | | | | |
| Damage | 89.2a[c] | .43a | 3.63a | .64a | 4.30a | .13a | .034a | .013a | .010ab | .00027a | .00065a |
| Non-damage | 90.2ab | .43a | 3.75a | .58a | 4.36a | .12a | .031a | .015a | .011ab | .00031a | .00060a |
| Western hemlock | | | | | | | | | | | |
| Damage | 89.2a | .65b | 1.97c | 1.62c | 3.67a | .13a | .033a | .021b | .013bc | .00042a | .0021b |
| Non-damage | 89.1a | .64b | 1.76c | 1.96c | 3.83a | .13a | .035a | .029b | .015c | .00044a | .0019b |
| Western redcedar | | | | | | | | | | | |
| Damage | 91.4b | .83c | .80b | 1.63c | 2.69b | .13a | .032a | .025b | .009a | .00042a | .00027c |
| Non-damage | 91.4b | .85c | .65b | 1.93c | 2.69b | .13a | .028a | .022b | .009a | .00045a | .00018c |
| Red alder | | | | | | | | | | | |
| Damage | 91.3b | 1.02c | 1.56c | .50a | 2.10c | .17b | .035a | .025b | .040b | .0012b | .00079a |
| Non-damage | 90.6ab | .91c | 1.45c | .43a | 1.80c | .22c | .030a | .025b | .032e | .0012b | .00074a |

[a]Values are averages of two composite samples from 10 trees each.

[b]Damage and non-damage areas are, respectively, north and south of the Chehalis River in Grays Harbor County, Washington.

[c]Means in each column followed by the same letter(s) do not differ significantly at the 5 percent level, with a modification of Tukey's test (Snedecor 1961).

55

concentration range of the sugars, calculated on a fresh-weight basis, was 1.80 to 4.36 percent. However, calculation to an organic-matter basis shows that the average concentrations of total sugars were 43, 37, 33 and 24 percent in Douglas-fir, western hemlock, western redcedar and red alder, respectively. Sugars, therefore, were one of the major organic constituents of the sapwood.

Three sugars were detected chromatographically: glucose, fructose and sucrose. In addition, visual examination of the chromatograms showed that in all extracts, concentrations of glucose and fructose were approximately equal. All sapwood samples, therefore, contained the same kinds of sugar and glucose/fructose ratio.

Total nitrogen content in sapwood ranged from 0.12 to 0.22 percent, indicating a low level of this element in the tissue. Regardless of the area, Douglas-fir, western hemlock and western redcedar contained similar amounts of this element. In contrast, red alder from the non-damage area was higher in nitrogen than that from the damage area. Also, the average nitrogen content for red alder sapwood of both areas at 0.20 percent was significantly higher than that in sapwood of the other three species. Within species, nitrogenous compounds detected by chromatography did not differ with area of collection. However, amounts and, to a lesser extent, kinds of nitrogenous compounds varied among the species.

Concentrations of some mineral elements known to be important in animal nutrition are shown in Table 22. For all samples, average concentrations of phosphorus (P), calcium (C), magnesium (Mg), iron (Fe) and manganese (Mn) were .032, .022, .017, .00059 and .00090 percent respectively.

With the exception of Mg in red alder, where sapwood from the damage area contained higher concentrations of the element than that from the non-damage area, contents of the individual elements within species did not differ with the area. Among species, there were no differences in the P contents and only a limited number of major differences in contents of the other elements. Thus, Douglas-fir was lowest in Ca, western hemlock highest in Mn, western redcedar lowest in Mn and red alder highest in Mg and Fe.

## Conclusions

The analysis of sapwood shows that sugar was a major nutrient component of the tissue and mineral elements and nitrogen occurred in minor amounts. Also, sapwood tissue was lower in mineral elements and nitrogen, but higher in sugar than vegetation which serves as bear food on the study areas (unpublished chemical analysis of red huckleberry ((*Vaccinium parvifolium*)) and salal shoots collected from the same areas and at the same time as tree sapwood). Thus, sapwood appeared to be a good source of sugar for bear.

On both areas, there were significant differences among species in content and kind of some chemical constituents, but total sugars and ash were the only components which seemed to be related to bear preference. High preference was generally associated with high sugar and low ash. Obviously, it is impossible to state conclusively that one, or a combination of these two

56

components, was actually responsible for the preference. However, one may speculate that sugar alone was the important factor. That sugar was apparently a major animal nutrient present in sapwood tends to support this speculation. Furthermore, sugar has long been recognized as extremely important in the nutrition and metabolism of animals (Fruton and Simmonds 1958), and has been suspected to be a factor in food preference of some animals (Plice 1952; Radwan and Campbell 1968). However, the fact that bear do not feed on tree sapwood south of the Chehalis River, despite the similar sugar content and the general chemical composition of sapwoods on the two study areas, is inconsistent with the sugar hypothesis or any other explanation of preference based on the data from this study. In addition, bear preference for trees is known to vary by state (Lutz 1951; Glover 1955; Zeedyk 1957) and even by area within western Washington.

In this study, therefore, chemical analysis alone was not sufficient to explain the problem of bear feeding on tree sapwood.


## SUMMARY

### Damage History

1.  The first serious bear damage in Washington was noted in 1942 when heavily damaged 30 to 40-year-old Douglas-fir were reported in a small area northwest of Hoquiam in Grays Harbor County.

2.  Occurrences of damage by black bear have been noted in most regions where timber has been a primary industry. Alaska, British Columbia, Oregon, California, Maine, Montana and Wyoming have all reported instances of damage.

### Damage Characteristics

1.  In Washington, Douglas-fir appears to be the most frequently damaged species. Damage is primarily to immature, smooth-barked trees. Damage generally occurs at the base of the tree, but may extend upwards 40 to 50 feet on occasion.

2.  Information gathered in 1963 revealed that bear damage was widely distributed over western Washington. Average dbh of damaged trees ranged from 9 to 15.6 inches in various areas. The 20 to 40-year class was most often damaged.

3.  Heavier bear damage occurs on better quality sites (Classes I, II and III). More lightly stocked areas receive the heaviest damage. Faster growing, more vigorous trees are damaged more frequently than others.

### Damage Effects

1.  Complete girdling of a tree results in death of the tree. Partial girdling may cause reduced growth or increased infection with subsequent decay and loss of wood volume at harvest.

2.  An investigation of bear damage-induced fungus infections indicated

that decay was more prevalent in Sitka spruce and western hemlock than in Douglas-fir. Decay was absent in 60.5 percent of infected Douglas-fir. Four brown rot, four white rot and one blue staining fungi were isolated from bear injuries.

    3. *Stereum sanguinolentum* and *Fomes annosus* were the predominant fungi isolated.

## Damage Survey Techniques

    1. Data on existent bear damage may be collected in conjunction with regular forest inventory cruises or by use of specific damage transects.

    2. Minimum data should include tree species present, whether damaged or not, dbh, age of damage, degree of girdle and whether damaged trees are injured or killed.

    3. Inventory and transect data regarding bear damage are important to the forest manager who recommends control programs and the wildlife manager who must limit control operations to those areas with substantiated damage.

## Tree Species Preferences

    1. Douglas-fir is the preferred species at low and intermediate elevations of western Washington.

    2. A preference rating may be determined with the formula:

$$\frac{\text{DK of Compared Species}}{\text{DK of Base Species}} \times 100 = \text{Preference Rating}$$

## Bear Damage Control

    1. The Washington Forest Protection Association (WFPA) is a trade association of private and municipal forestland owners.

    2. The WFPA organized a cooperative bear damage control program in 1960.

    3. Professional bear control is accomplished primarily with the Aldrich Spring Activated Animal Snare coupled with a miniature radio transmitter which emits a pulsating signal when the snare is sprung.

    4. Control operations are conducted only in specific areas for which special damage control permits have been issued.

## Vegetation Inventory

    1. In the non-damage study area key spring food items of black bear represented a frequency of 23.5 percent and canopy coverage of 21.4 percent. On the damage study area key spring food items represented a frequency of 26.4 percent and canopy coverage of 24.4 percent.

## Sapwood Analysis

1.  Sugar was found to be a major nutrient component of sapwood tissue. Mineral elements and nitrogen occurred in minor amounts. Sapwood was higher in sugar content than either red huckleberry or salal.

2.  The fact that bear did not feed on sapwood in the non-damage study area despite the similar sugar content and general chemical composition of sapwoods on the two study areas, precluded any explanation of bear damage based on these data.

# SECTION II

# NATURAL HISTORY

# RELOCATION DISTANCES AND OCCUPIED AREAS OF EAR-TAGGED AND RADIO-COLLARED BEAR

Two methods were employed to study the movement of individual black bear. One involved ear-tagging captured bear with numbered metal tags and colored vinyl ribbons, the other monitoring of radio-collared bear. It was hoped that subsequent observation of ear-tagged bear in the field would provide sufficient information to document their movement patterns. Although much good information was collected from these bear it was mostly acquired when the bear was killed by hunters and not, as was hoped for, by frequent, repeated observation of bear in the field. To obtain information on the movement of individual bear over a period of time, it was necessary to develop a system for locating bear by radio-monitoring as they pursued their normal activities. Results of these activities follow.

## EAR-TAGGED BEAR

During the years 1964 through 1966, 38 black bear were captured, ear-tagged with numbered metal tags and colored vinyl streamers and released at or near point of capture. Fourteen of these were from the damage, and 24 from the non-damage study area. Of 25 males, 10 were from the damage and 15 from the non-damage study area. Of 13 females, 4 were from the damage and 9 from the non-damage study area. Twenty-six of these bear were relocated a total of 32 times either through sightings, capture or kills by May, 1971. Two bear were relocated twice and two others were relocated three times. All other bear were relocated one time. Two of the one-time relocations were to the general area of original capture only, and could not be used in distance computations.

Time between release and subsequent relocation varied from .1 to 83.5 months with an average of 18 months. No relation between relocation distance and time lapse between release and relocation was noted. This is in agreement with similar observations by Erickson and Petrides (1964). Fifteen relocations were based on the termination point of hunts with dogs. Information available on seven of these hunts showed that they began an average of 2.8, and terminated an average of 3.0 miles, from release sites. No bias effect from relocations based on hound hunts was apparent. Average relocation time lapse for males was 20 months and for females, 15 months.

Mean relocation distances for 24 black bear are shown in Figure 19. Two characteristics of black bear travels are disclosed: one is the wider-ranging habits of males as compared to females, and the second, of particular interest in this study, the wider ranging of both males and females in the damage study

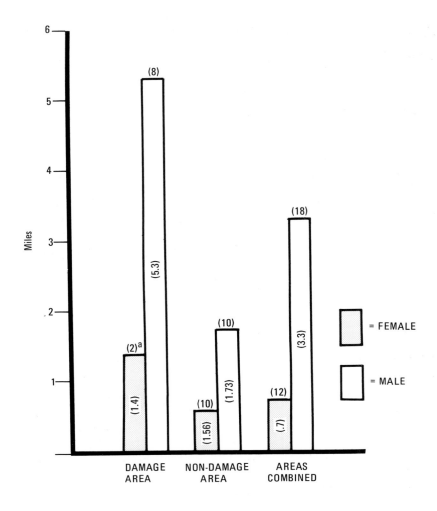

aNumber of Relocations

FIG. 19.-- Mean relocation distances of 24 ear-tagged western Washington black bear in damage and non-damage study areas with age classes combined and sexes compared.

area as compared to bear in the non-damage study area. This greater ranging lends support to a hypothesis on the cause of bear damage to conifers being related to a shortage of preferred food items in their habitat. Greater ranging being theoretically a reflection of more intensive searching for food in the damage as compared to the non-damage study area. The longest relocation distance was for an adult male in the damage area killed 14.5 miles from the release site. This compares with the longest movement recorded by Erickson and Petrides (1964) of 19.4 miles for a female accompanied by a cub. Data on all age classes were combined for these computations because of limited data on cubs and yearlings. Three yearlings relocated during the study did, how-ever, appear to range less than older bear, as all relocation distances exceeding 3 miles were from subadult and adult bear. Longest relocation distances for 24 black bear are shown in Figure 20.

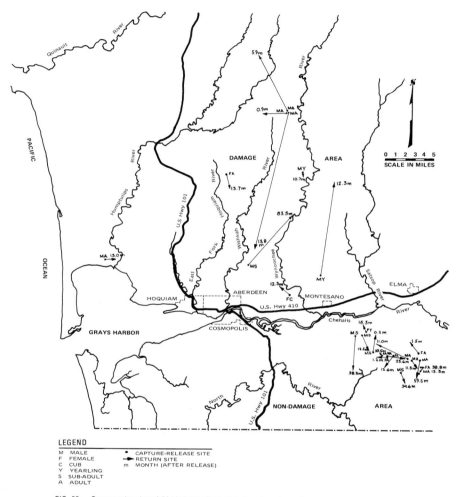

FIG. 20.-- Greatest relocation of 24 black bear from original capture-release sites, based on observation, recapture and kill returns, 1964 through 1971.

No incidence of movement between the damage and non-damage study areas was noted. Minimum distance for release sites between the two areas was 6 miles. This lack of emigration suggests a possible relationship between the bear's somewhat restricted ranging and the tree damage problem. Minimal emigration of black bear was reported by Erickson and Petrides (1964) and Jonkel and Cowan (1971). Insufficient data were obtained to allow drawing any conclusions with regard to a damage relationship.

63

As an adjunct to these observations bear control personnel provided three additional bear relocations in areas outside the study areas. An adult male from the north Olympic Peninsula was recovered approximately 2 miles from its release site 2 years later. Two subadult males, tagged and released in southwestern Washington, were recovered 1.2 and 11.6 months later at distances of 0.8 and 2.5 miles, respectively, from their release sites.

Relocation data from ear-tagged black bear in this study suggests that they remain in the same general area from year to year and that emigration is not common. Erickson and Petrides (1964) found that black bear tended to remain in the same general area from year to year in Michigan.

Comparison of data obtained in other states with that in Washington shows some general similarities (Table 23). Females in each study moved lesser distances than did the males. Relocation distances of males in Washington, Montana and Michigan were similar. Average distances moved by male black bear in Wisconsin and Virginia were considerably greater than in Washington. In New York, 40 black bear, not defined by sex or age class, released within one mile of their capture site, were recovered an average of 3.6 miles from the release point within one year (Black 1958).

TABLE 23.—Comparison of relocation data from five separate studies of black bear.

| Study location | Number of Male/Female | Relocation distance in miles | | | |
| | | Male | | Female | |
| | | Mean | Maximum | Mean | Maximum |
|---|---|---|---|---|---|
| Western Washington | 16/8 | 3.3 | 14.5 | 0.7 | 1.5 |
| Montana (Jonkel and Cowan 1971) | 16/31 | 3.9 | 5.7 | 1.6 | 2.5 |
| Wisconsin (Knudsen 1961) | 28/15 | 15.5 | 46.0 | <2.0 | 36.0[a] |
| Michigan (Erickson and Petrides 1964) | 10/7 | 5.4 | 11.9 | 1.4 | 19.4[a] |
| Virginia (Stickley 1961) | 21/7 | 10.0 | 90.0[a] | 1.8 | . . |

[a] Aberrant movement by a single bear not included in mean relocation distance.

## RADIO-COLLARED BEAR

A need existed to determine, at least in a general way, the movement patterns of individual black bear over a period of time. This information was required if objective management decisions concerning black bear were to be reached with respect to both sport hunting and control of tree damage. Dense forests and heavy underbrush characteristic of western Washington black bear habitat precluded successful use of ear-tagged black bear for this purpose. Radio-tracking was identified as the only available means to provide adequate information on these movements. At the time of the study, radio-tracking was relatively new, and no such studies had been done with black bear. System development began in 1963 and culminated in monitoring of bear from spring of 1965 to early spring 1967.

On-the-shelf products were not readily available. Much of the system and associated equipment was designed and assembled by communications specialists from the Washington State Department of Natural Resources and project personnel.

## Monitoring System

Two vehicle mounted receivers were used. Each vehicle had non-directional, whip-type antennae for general surveillance or signal searching. One vehicle was equipped with a roof-mounted, fold-down, directional loop antenna, which could be rotated from inside the vehicle (Fig. 21). These receivers were powered through a convertor from the vehicle battery.

FIG. 21.—Radio monitoring vehicle equipped with directional loop antenna.

Two transistorized, battery powered, hand-tracking receivers were used, each with a directional antenna.

One large double element yagi antenna, mounted on a 60-foot tower which could be rotated from the ground, was employed on the summit of a mountain (Minot Peak, elevation 1,768 feet) for general surveillance of bear in the non-damage area. A single element yagi antenna was mounted on the roof of a small building in the same area for surveillance of a specific bear.

Collar type transmitters were used with the antenna encircling the neck (Figs. 22, 23, 24, and 25). Radio components were mounted compactly on a small fiberglass board, and took up slightly more than one cubic inch. Copper strips, approximately ⅜-inches wide, extended from two opposite sides of the component mounting board. These served as the transmitting antenna. As a collar unit, the copper strips were bent around the neck and united at the top, while the radio component package hung underneath. In early models, when small batteries were used, batteries were mounted on the copper strips on each side of the radio package and the strips enclosed with braided nylon rope. In later models, when as many as six large batteries (same size as common "D" flashlight battery) were used, the primary transmitter was backed by a thick nylon belt about 1 ½ inches wide, which served to distribute collar weight around the top of the bear's neck, and as a broad base of attachment for the larger batteries. To reduce malfunctions, radio components were embedded in rigid plastic. Batteries and wiring were coated with flexible plastic material.

**FIG. 22.—Collar type radio transmitter ready for attachment on bear.**

The entire transmitter collar was bound with black electrician's tape, leaving only the ends of the copper antenna uncovered. The transmitter, as originally designed, functioned only within a narrow range with respect to antenna (collar) length. In practical terms, this meant that the transmitter would have to be fabricated after the bear was captured, or else several collars of varying sizes would have to be on hand to accommodate the neck size of any bear captured. This feature required correction before the monitoring system could be used in the field. Pulsation of the transmitter, at any given range in antenna circumference, was dependent on the resistance value of a single capacitor. By providing for this component to be changed after attaching the collar to the bear, the problem was solved. In practice, the collar, minus the capacitor, was fitted around the bear's neck and the two segments of the copper antenna were soldered securely at the top of the neck. This soldered area was then wrapped with tape. The final step was to select the proper capacitor, which was determined when a pulse signal occurred that did not cease when the circular antenna was moderately disfigured intentionally. The capacitor was soldered to two circuit wires left protruding from the component package, then secured in place by applying a small amount of quick hardening plastic and more tape. The first collars were black and weighed between one and two pounds. Later collars, with larger batteries, were considerably heavier and bulkier. They were painted white for ease of observation. The largest collars, weighing over 4 pounds, proved satisfactory on bear exceeding 150 pounds.

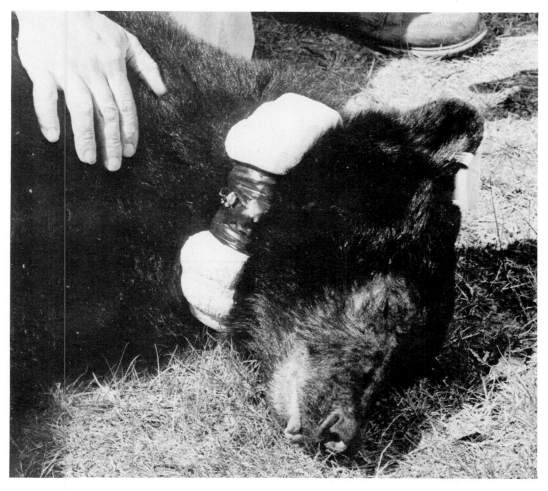

**FIG. 23.—Subadult female black bear fitted with collar-type radio transmitter.**

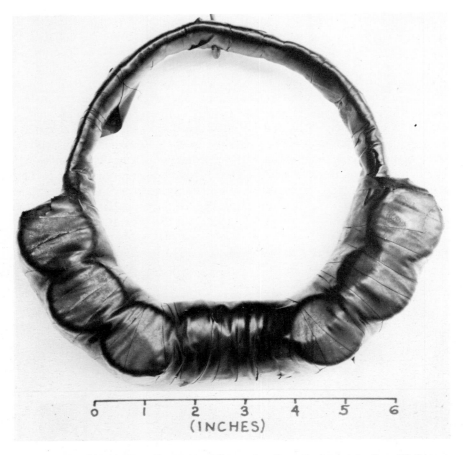

**FIG. 24.—Radio transmitter from a yearling male after attachment in the wild from August 25, 1965 to July 16, 1966.**

The monitoring system was designed to operate in the 30 megacycle range. Six assigned frequencies allowed minimum interference from other communication systems, and separation of signals from different bear in a particular area. Reception was line of sight. With the mobile receivers and whip antennae, signals could be heard distinctly at distances up to 10 miles. Normal operational monitoring generally occurred at distances less than one mile.

Approximate locations of radio-equipped bear were determined by surveillance, either with the mobile tracking units or the stationary yagi antennae. Mobile units were superior for this purpose and were generally operated by two-man teams. Once the general location was determined, the next stop was to secure a precise location. This was determined by taking compass bearings on the signal source with directional loop antennae from several well distributed points detectable on maps or aerial photographs. Most triangulation was done with hand-tracking equipment. The mobile mounted loop antenna, connected to a highly sensitive receiver, enabled triangulation at greater distances

68

than the less sensitive hand-tracking receivers. Detailed information on activities and locations of bear was obtained by moving in close to bear with hand-tracking equipment. Once a transmitter was attached, special effort was made to maintain contact with the animal and monitor it as frequently as possible during the operating life of the transmitter.

**FIG. 25.—Subadult female showing attachment of radio transmitter at time of release.**

As a continuous signal would rapidly deplete the limited power supply, transmitters were designed to emit a pulse signal. Variations in construction of transmitters caused different pulse rates by which different instrumented bear, ranging in the same area, were readily identified. This factor supplemented separation of individual bear by different frequencies. Wave emission from a collar-type antenna varies widely in relation to the plane of the antenna. The signal is strongest in line with the plane and gradually becomes weaker approaching the perpendicular (null point) of the plane. As a result, signal strength is variable when an instrumented bear is moving (weaving its head from side to side) but constant when not moving. This feature, either alone or in combination with data from triangulation or close-in monitoring, provided bear activity data not otherwise obtainable. Directional loop antennae receive radio waves in the same manner that collar antennae transmit them. Reception is strongest in line with the plane of the loop, and there is practically no reception (null point) perpendicular to the loop. The null is so sharply distinctive at an acute angle that it is used to determine an azimuth on the signal source. In practice, a compass bearing is taken on a distant landmark in line with the null. This bearing, however, is bi-directional; the signal source can be anywhere on the line indicated by the null, either behind or in front of the antenna. The actual direction is resolved by triangulation, by attempts to move closer to the signal source and by relating effects of local terrain features on signal strength. Locations on null points were quite accurate up to a transmission distance of one-half mile; beyond this, accuracy decreased.

Blocking of signals by land masses was the most serious monitoring problem. This was intensified by the fact that most instrumented bear occupied rugged terrain and ranged in areas remote from access roads. The null point from directional loop antennae could not be detected from weak signals. That bear habitually ranged in a given general area, even though large, was a factor that made monitoring less difficult. Whenever a signal could not be heard in the habitual range of the animal, an attempt was made to monitor the general area by aircraft. It was possible to locate bear in an area the size of a football field by rapid changes in signal strength during low-level passes.

Several transmitters developed a common malfunction, changing from a normal pulse to a constant, non-pulsing signal. This malfunction drained electrical energy rapidly, made determination of activity status more difficult and was often mistaken for similar interference sounds. The problem was reduced by more rigid construction of the antenna portion of the collar in the second year.

Signals were often deflected from a straight line in certain areas, especially at close range in dense timber. This problem, while not common, was resolved by taking several bearings or by moving in close to verify locations.

Another problem was monitoring capability. During the first year several bear were instrumented in a short time. This resulted in spreading the monitoring effect over too many bear with a reduction in the number of relocations of individual bear. A lesser number of bear were instrumented the second year to allow more efficient monitoring.

## Instrumented Bear

Sixteen bear were radio-collared, 11 in 1965 and 5 in 1966. Seven of these bear were from the damage and nine from the non-damage study area. Ten were males, five from each study area, and six were females, four from the damage and two from the non-damage study area. Nine of these bear were successfully monitored for periods of 1.8 to 7.1 months. One bear lost the collar and two were relocated only 2 or 3 times shortly following release, and then never heard again. Four bear were never monitored following release. Of the nine bear successfully monitored, five were males, two from the damage

70

and three from the non-damage study area, and four were females, all from the non-damage study area. The first nine bear were instrumented in the field; the remainder were transported to a holding cage for instrumentation then returned to the capture area for release. Attaching transmitters in captivity provided greater assurance that they were functioning properly at release. Successful operation of the transmitters was dependent on proper execution of three steps: (1) the ends of the copper strips had to be securely soldered, (2) the correct capacitor selected and attached, and (3) the collar had to be fitted properly to ensure it would not be removed by the bear.

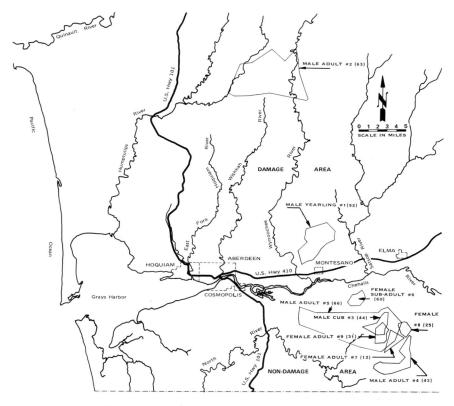

FIG. 26.- - Areas occupied by 9 radio-collared black bear in western Washington. Number in parentheses indicates number of relocations on which area is based.

## Areas Occupied

A summary of relocation data on the nine bear successfully monitored is given in Table 24. Limited data precludes comparison of bear in the damage and non-damage study areas. Bear Number 3, a male cub, was used to reflect the movements of its mother which the cub accompanied. Areas occupied by each bear were established by connecting outermost monitored locations for

71

TABLE 24.—Relocation data on nine radio-collared black bear monitored in western Washington.

| Bear No. | Sex/Age class[a] | Capture date | Period(s) monitored | Days monitored | Number of relocations located | Total days located | Mean relocation distance[b] | Square mile area occupied | Greatest distance between all locations[b] |
|---|---|---|---|---|---|---|---|---|---|
| 1[c] | M/Y | 7/ 7/65 | 7/ 7: 8/ 4 8/27:11/19 | 114 | 52 | 41 | 1.38 | 8.9 | 6.90 |
| 2[c] | M/A | 5/26/66 | 5/31: 9/27 | 89 | 63 | 47 | 2.16 | 31.9 | 8.70 |
| 3[d] | M/C | 8/31/65 | 9/ 4:10/27 | 54 | 44 | 33 | .66 | 2.5 | 3.15 |
| 4 | M/A | 4/27/66 | 4/30: 7/27 | 89 | 43 | 39 | 1.46 | 5.2 | 5.25 |
| 5 | M/A | 6/13/65 | 6/13: 9/ 2 (1965) 5/ 6: 8/ 1 (1966) | 171 | 66 | 53 | 1.34 | 33.6 | 11.00 |
| 6 | F/S | 5/31/65 | 9/13/66 to 4/14/67 | 214 | 60 | 55 | .74 | 2.1 | 2.25 |
| 7 | F/A | 6/16/65 | 6/16: 9/15 | 92 | 12 | 12 | 1.55 | 2.2 | 2.60 |
| 8 | F/A | 6/13/65 | 6/13: 8/13 | 62 | 25 | 20 | .73 | 1.3 | 1.70 |
| 9 | F/A | 5/26/65 | 5/26: 7/27 | 63 | 31 | 23 | .61 | 2.1 | 2.46 |
| Damage area males (less cub) | | | | | | | 1.77 | 20.4 | |
| Non-damage area males | | | | | | | 1.40 | 19.4 | |
| All males (less cub) | | | | | | | 1.58 | 19.9 | |
| Non-damage area females | | | | | | | .86 | 2.04 | |

[a] M(male), F(female),/A(adult), S(subadult), Y(yearling), C(cub)
[b] Relocation distance (distance between consecutive relocations) in miles.
[c] Damage study area. All other from non-damage study area.
[d] Data used to reflect movement of adult female which cub followed.

72

the individual bear as placed on a map. Because of variations in total time period monitored, numbers of relocations for individual bear, seasons monitored and intensity of monitoring effort, neither territorial nor home range status is ascribed to these occupied areas. Males ranged over distinctly larger areas than females, averaging 19.9 and 2.04 square miles respectively. No overlap in occupied areas of adult males was noted. Areas occupied by females overlapped with those of males and occasionally with other females. No conflict between bear occupying overlapping areas was noted. Diagrams of areas occupied by each monitored bear are shown in Figure 26. These occupied areas are based on as few as 12 to as many as 66 monitored relocations. Elapsed time between first and last monitoring ranged from 54 to 214 days. Monitoring periods for individual bear occurred variously in early spring, summer, late fall and winter. Mean relocation distance is based on locations determined at least 6 hours apart. As of this writing, only Bear Number 2 and 6 are unaccounted for. All others have been killed by hunters.

Home ranges of ear-tagged black bear were determined by Jonkel and Cowan (1971) as that area in which each bear was regularly captured or observed from year to year. Overlapping of home ranges between adult males and adult females was noted but was minimal between adults of the same sex. Observations by Jonkel and Cowan (1971) supported the contention that emigration by adult bear from areas normally occupied was not common. Because of the linearity of habitat and extremes of elevation on their study area, they estimated home ranges based on measured movements. Greatest movements averaged 1.6 miles for adult females and 3.9 miles for adult males. Erickson and Petrides (1964) determined home ranges of black bear on the assumptions that home ranges are circular and that recoveries indicate normal cruising diameters. Average minimal summer and annual ranges determined in their study of ear-tagged animals were 6 and 15 square miles, respectively. Ranges of adult males were about a third greater and those of females about a third smaller than the averages. Thus, male home ranges were about twice the size of female home ranges. Spencer (1955) attributed a home range of approximately 78 square miles to black bear in Maine. He concluded that there was a great deal of overlapping of ranges with very little conflict.

## Diurnal Behavior

Twenty-one relocations of six different bear were made during hours of darkness. Seventeen of these relocations showed the bear to be inactive for extended periods. Of 347 daytime relocations, not associated with denning behavior, bear were recorded inactive only 28 times. These data suggest a diurnal behavior pattern for western Washington black bear. These data are in disagreement with the nocturnal behavior attributed to the black bear by Erickson (1965). Other authors have attributed varying degrees of nocturnal and diurnal behavior to the black bear based on food sources such as garbage dumps and campgrounds (Bloomfield 1964) or whether they existed in an area inhabited by grizzlies (Wright 1910). The normally secretive and solitary habits of the black bear, together with his heavily wooded habitat, have kept sightings to a minimum in many areas and undoubtedly lent support to the thesis that they are primarily nocturnal. Future radio-monitoring studies of black bear, one of which is now in progress, should clarify this point, at least for black bear in western Washington.

## Denning Behavior

Of the nine bear monitored, only three were monitored beyond the end of September, Bear Numbers 1, 3 and 6. Bear Number 1 was monitored until 19 November at which time it was still active. It had, however, remained inactive from 14 to 17 November while asleep in a hollow log. Bear Number 3 was killed on 27 October and had shown no periods of inactivity suggestive of denning activity. Bear Number 6 was monitored over the winter period, 1966-67. Evidence of beginning of dormancy was recorded on 9 November when the animal was aroused from a prolonged period of inactivity during daylight hours. Complete dormancy was recorded between 28 November and 21 February. During this period the bear was aroused from den locations nine times by investigators. A period of mixed activity and inactivity was noted between 27 February and 30 March. Complete activity was noted by 7 April. Four den sites were located. Two were in hollow logs, one was in an excavated cavity at the base of a large, rotten stump and one was in a natural cavity at the base of a bigleaf maple tree. No bedding material was used. The bear moved to a new den site each time she was aroused. Distance from vacated to new den site ranged from .12 to .87 miles. Three vacated sites were subsequently used again. Dense ground cover appeared to be preferred at the den site. Three dens were within a few hundred feet of forest access roads. Only one brief snowfall occurred during the denning period. Temperatures in the vicinity of dens ranged from 34 to 50 degrees Fahrenheit. This bear was invariably aware of investigators as they approached the den sites. The closest approach prior to the bear's departure from the den was 30 feet. Although these data represent definite denning behavior in only one bear, they do establish, for the first time, that some western Washington black bear do have a dormant period of nearly three months, even in relatively mild winters. Winter denning periods established for black bear in other localities are shown in Table 25. Pictures of two black bear den sites not associated with tagged bear are shown in Figures 27 and 28. Each was discovered by non-project personnel.

TABLE 25.—Approximate winter denning dates for black bear.

| Authority | Location | Denning dates |
|---|---|---|
| Hatler (1967) | Alaska | Early to mid-October to early May |
| Erickson (1965) | Alaska | Late October to April or later |
| Erickson (1964) | Michigan | Mid-November to mid-April |
| Gilbert (1952) | Colorado | Early November to late March or early April |
| Jonkel and Cowan (1971) | Montana | Early November to mid-May |
| Spencer (1955) | Maine | December to early April |

**FIG. 27.—Den where abandoned cubs (Fig. 41) were found.**

FIG. 28.—Den of adult female accompanied by two yearlings in hollowed butt of Douglas-fir tree.

# REPRODUCTION

Reproduction in the black bear is one of the most interesting aspects of its biology. A concurrent summary of the general pattern of reproductive physiology and behavior of both sexes, from emergence from the den in one year to emergence the next, follows. This information is based on published literature. Following this summarization data collected during the Cooperative Black Bear Study will be presented.

**PRE-BREEDING SEASON**

When the non-pregnant female retires to her den in early winter, her ovaries are in what can best be called a quiescent state. No marked differences

76

can be detected between ovaries of non-pregnant mature or immature females during this late non-breeding state (Erickson and Nellor 1964). Increased ovarian activity in March and April precedes follicular development. Growth of follicles is noted during April and May. They do not, however, reach a mature size. Follicles in the mature animal achieve maximum size (8 to 12 mm in diameter) just prior to the breeding season in late May or early June (op. cit.). These follicles can at times be noted as slight protuberances or raised areas on the surface of the ovary (Wimsatt 1963).

By the time the male has retired to his winter den he has undergone extensive testicular atrophy. Testicular recrudesence, reactivation of gonadal tissues, is advanced prior to emergence. Gonadal activity of the male, including spermatogenesis, precedes and exceeds the period of acceptance by the female (Erickson and Nellor 1964).

## BREEDING SEASON

The peak of the breeding season extends generally from mid-June to mid-July (Wimsatt 1963; Erickson and Nellor 1964; Jonkel and Cowan 1971). At this time mature follicles are present in the ovaries of females and spermatogenic activity is present in the male.

Field observation of estrus in the female is based primarily on the presence of a swollen and inflamed vulva. The female has a seasonally constant estrus (Erickson and Nellor 1964). That is, she remains in heat until bred or, failing contact with a male, until ovarian degeneration. Estrus extends at least from May 25 to August 10 in some populations (Jonkel and Cowan 1971). Post-breeding heat is thought to be short (Erickson and Nellor 1964). Ovulation is induced through breeding (op. cit.). Thus, the presence of corpora lutea in the ovaries, formed following ovulation, is an indication of breeding. In the absence of breeding, mature follicles degenerate without ovulation. In examination of 56 bear, simultaneous occurrence of corpora lutea and large follicles was never noted (Wimsatt 1963).

Age of maturity probably varies somewhat with latitude in accordance with expected differences in the rate of growth (Rausch 1961). No bear less than 4.5 years of age were observed in estrus in Montana, nor were any litters successfully produced by females known to be less than 6.5 to 7.5 years of age (Jonkel and Cowan 1971). Three females, estimated to be 1.5 years old, were noted in heat in Virginia (Stickley 1961). Puberty for both sexes was reached at 3.5 years in Michigan (Erickson and Nellor 1964). Sexual maturity for wild male black bear was attained during the 5th or 6th summer in Alaska (Rausch 1961). Females which are lactating do not develop mature follicles, exhibit estrus nor accept males during the breeding season (Erickson and Nellor 1964). Estrus is apparently inhibited by a hormonal state associated with lactation which is maintained by the nursing stimulus. This lactation anestrus explains in part the alternate year pregnancies typical of black bear. Interruption of lactation for as short a period as two days may initiate estrus and allow consecutive year pregnancies (op. cit.). Consecutive year breeding was reported by Baker (1912) for sows which had cubs of the year removed prior to the breeding season.

77

Mating patterns from monogamy (Cockrum 1962) to polygamy (Stickley 1961), to promiscuous (Gilbert, pers. comm. cited in Bray and Barnes 1967), have been reported. Two factors are important with respect to male black bear under natural conditions: (1) Several female black bear are often present within the larger area normally occupied by the male, and (2) spermatogenic activity in the male precedes and exceeds the period of receptivity in the female. These factors suggest the possibility of a pattern of limited polygamy for the male. The suggested short-post-breeding heat of females and consequent lack of receptivity to males, would preclude polygamous behavior on her part.

## POST-BREEDING SEASON

Cessation of estrus occurs following breeding or at the onset of follicular degeneration in the absence of breeding. Testicular atrophy in the male occurs 1-2 months following the end of the general period of female receptivity (Erickson and Nellor 1964). Following breeding, mature follicles rupture, ova are released and fertilization occurs. Not all mature follicles present ovulate (op. cit.). Multiple ovulations seem for the most part to be confined to one ovary, indicating that in most cases one ovary is more active than the other during the breeding season (op. cit.). Follicles which do not ovulate are replaced by luteal-type activity. Corpora lutea formed after ovulation are maintained to term and are not discernable following parturition (op. cit.). The persistence of both corpora lutea and placental scars following pregnancy provide a means for the estimation of ovulation and conception rates. An ovulation rate of 2.4 per breeding was noted by Erickson and Nellor (1964) in Michigan, and by Stickley (1961) in Virginia, and 1.8 per breeding by Jonkel and Cowan (1971) in Montana. The earliest corpora lutea formation noted was 20 July in Michigan. Nearly all mature females without cubs studied in Michigan which had access to males showed corpora lutea formation following the breeding season.

Gestation is approximately 220 days (Wimsatt 1963). Following fertilization the embryo develops to the blastocyst stage where development is either arrested or slowed considerably and implantation deferred until about 1 December (op. cit.).

Rapid embryonic development occurs during the 6 to 8 weeks following implantation until parturition in late January or early February. Corpora lutea increase in volume 2 to 4.5 times during this post-implantation phase (op. cit.). Other examples of delayed implantation are found in fisher (Eadie and Hamilton 1958) and marten (Marshall and Enders 1942). Implantation sites in the reproductive tract are noted by the presence of placental scars. Lighter scars are ascribed to earlier pregnancies while darker, more distinct scars are from recent pregnancies (Erickson and Nellor 1964). Multiple implantations are characteristically divided between both horns of the tract. This, together with the fact that multiple ovulations are generally from a single ovary, suggest transmigration of embryos from one horn to the other (op. cit.).

Litter sizes ranging from 1.6 in Montana, to 2.6 in Virginia have been reported (Table 26). A litter of two cubs is the most common. Litter frequencies (percent of all females noted which had cubs) from 0 to 40 percent, with an eight-year average of 16 percent were reported by Jonkel and Cowan (1971) in Montana. Stickley (1961) reported a 48 percent frequency in Virginia. Data by Jonkel and Cowan (1971) suggest that habitat quality, particularly food availability, may have a primary role in long-term population control through its effect on the reproduction.

TABLE 26.—Litter sizes in black bear.

| Authority | Location | Mean litter size |
|-----------|----------|------------------|
| Jonkel and Cowan | Montana | 1.6[a] |
| (1971) | | 1.7[b] |
| Hatler (1967) | Alaska | 1.73 |
| Erickson and Nellor (1964) | Michigan | 2.04 |
| Spencer (1955) | Maine | 2.4 |
| Stickley (1961) | Virginia | 2.6[c] |

[a]Statewide average.
[b]Big Creek Study Area.
[c]Based on cub and embryo counts.

# COOPERATIVE BLACK BEAR STUDY REPRODUCTIVE DATA

Reproductive data were collected primarily from bear taken during control operations. Estrous condition of females was based on presence or absence of vulva swelling. Incidence of females with cubs was based on actual observation of accompanying cubs or occurrence of lactation. Female reproductive tracts were examined to determine ovulation and implantation rates. As the black bear is an induced ovulator, the presence of corpora lutea was used to establish ovulation rates. Ovaries were sectioned at 3 mm intervals for identification of corpora lutea. Mature follicles, while indicators of potential ovulation, were not included in this determination. Uterine cornu were opened and examined for presence or absence of placental scars. These scars indicate implantation sites of blastocysts from previous pregnancies. Variations in placental scar coloration result from effects of fixatives and from fading as the scars age (Erickson and Nellor 1964). While color variations indicated that scars in some uteri may have been from more recent pregnancies than those in other uteri, no objective criteria were established which could accurately age the scars. Simultaneous occurrence of scars with apparently differing ages was not noted. Ovulation and implantation rates are indicators of breeding and maximum possible litter size. No informationon parturition rate or pre-emergence mortality was obtained. Known-age bear are those which have had ages ascribed based on counts of cementum layers. Other bear were aged on the basis of tooth eruption and wear, body size and gross physical appearance. No detailed information on male reproductive activity was obtained.

## Female Reproduction

During the period April through October in 1964, 1965 and 1966, 378 female black bear collected in western Washington were examined for externally visible indications of reproductive activity and recorded as in estrus, lactating or inactive. All were estimated to be at least two years old. Results are shown in Table 27. Average yearly lactation rates ranged from 10 percent in 1966 to 24 percent in 1964. The range of estrous rates was much less, 24 percent in 1965 and 1966, to 29 percent in 1964. Average lactation rate for the three year period was 16 percent and average estrous rate was 26 percent. This lactation rate compares with the 16 percent litter frequency found in Montana by Jonkel and Cowan (1971). Subsequent to these determinations, 22 bear from this group were found to be 3 ½ years old or older and thus were considered as sexually mature. If this correction factor is applied to the estrous and lactation rates for the entire sample, eliminating the sexually immature from the sample, a lactation rate of 19 percent and an estrous rate of 31 percent apply. Bear were collected throughout their active period from April to October. Lactation would normally extend through this time frame, and thus the lactation rates found can be considered accurate. The same is not true of estrous determinations. Many of the bear collected which did not show

TABLE 27.—Reproductive condition of 378 female black bear, estimated to be two years old or older, collected in western Washington during the period April through October, in 1964, 1965 and 1966.

| Location | Year | % Lactating | % in Estrus[a] | Neither | Total sample |
|---|---|---|---|---|---|
| Grays Harbor | 1964 | 10(2)[b] | 45(8) | 45(8) | 18 |
| Area | 1965 | 7(2) | 43(13) | 50(15) | 30 |
| | 1966 | 13(2) | 25(4) | 62(10) | 16 |
| North Olympic | 1964 | 15(10) | 37(23) | 48(30) | 63 |
| Peninsula | 1965 | 16(11) | 20(13) | 64(44) | 68 |
| | 1966 | 4(2) | 41(19) | 55(26) | 47 |
| Southwest | 1964 | 32(5) | 32(5) | 36(6) | 16 |
| Washington | 1965 | 20(2) | 10(1) | 70(7) | 10 |
| | 1966 | 6(1) | 0(0) | 94(17) | 18 |
| South Puget | 1964 | 42(15) | 5(2) | 53(19) | 36 |
| Sound Basin | 1965 | 5(2) | 15(6) | 80(31) | 39 |
| | 1966 | 29(5) | 0(0) | 71(12) | 17 |
| Combined % | 1964 | 24(32) | 29(38) | 47(63) | 133 |
| for western | 1965 | 12(17) | 24(36) | 64(94) | 147 |
| Washington | 1966 | 10(10) | 24(23) | 66(65) | 98 |
| 3-year Average for western Washington | | 16 | 26 | 58 | 378 |

[a]Based on observed incidence of vulva swelling.
[b]Number in parenthesis is sample size.

80

visible signs of estrus may well have been collected prior to or after vulva swelling occurred. Thus, the incidence of estrus is probably underestimated. Unsuccessful breeding, mortality during embryonic development, or post-parturition death of cubs prior to emergence from the den are factors which probably contribute to the lactation rate being lower than the estrous rate. Variations in percent of females lactating from year to year reflect fluctuating reproductive rates or fecundity of the population. Similar variations were reported by Jonkel and Cowan (1971) in Montana. Although their data were not conclusive, they did note that decreases in natality followed poor berry years, while increased natality followed good berry years. While some similar environmental factor may have been operative in the Washington population, no supporting data are available. Results from 97 estrous female black bear, estimated to be two years old or older, are shown in Figure 29. In Washington, the peak of estrus was reached in late June and maintained into July. This peak is comparable with that in other regions (Jonkel and Cowan 1971; Erickson and Nellor 1964).

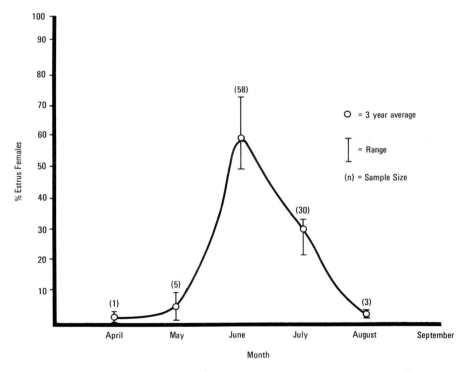

FIG. 29.- - Month of estrus for 97 female black bear, 2 years old or older, collected in western Washington during 1964, 1965 and 1966 based on incidence of vulva swelling.

Reproductive tracts of 24 known-age bear were examined to determine the incidence of placental scars and presence of corpora lutea (Table 28 and Fig. 30). Sexual maturity, based on corpora lutea development, was evidenced by 44 percent of the females in their fourth summer. All females 5 ½ years old or older had either placental scars or developed corpora lutea and thus were considered sexually mature. The youngest age of confirmed corpora lutea development, indicative of successful breeding and ovulation, was 3.4 years (Bear No. 4591). Corpora lutea were found in three other 3 ½-year-old bear. While only two 4.4-year-old bear were in the sample, one did show recent placental scars, confirming further that sexual maturity for some female black bear in Washington is achieved during their fourth summer. The remaining

TABLE 28.—Reproduction data from 24 known-age[a] female black bear collected during 1964, 1965 and 1966 in western Washington.

| Specimen Number | Collection Date | Age | Bred | Placental Scars | | Corpora Lutea | |
|---|---|---|---|---|---|---|---|
| | | | | Left Cornu | Right Cornu | Left Ovary | Right Ovary |
| F-34 | 6/23 | 1.4 | No | 0 | 0 | 0 | 0 |
| J-32 | 6/29 | 1.4 | No | 0 | 0 | 0 | 0 |
| 4589 | 6/15 | 2.4 | No | 0 | 0 | 0 | 0 |
| 4510 | 6/1 | 3.3 | No | 0 | 0 | 0 | 0 |
| 4511 | 6/2 | 3.3 | No | 0 | 0 | 0 | 0 |
| 4591 | 6/16 | 3.4 | Yes | 0 | 0 | 2 | 0 |
| 4574 | 6/28 | 3.4 | Yes | 0 | 0 | 1 | 0 |
| 4522 | 6/29 | 3.4 | No | 0 | 0 | 0 | 0 |
| 4523 | 6/29 | 3.4 | No | 0 | 0 | 0 | 0 |
| 4533 | 8/26 | 3.6 | Yes | 0 | 0 | 0 | 2 |
| 4527 | 9/9 | 3.6 | No | 0 | 0 | 0 | 0 |
| 4507 | 9/11 | 3.6 | Yes | 0 | 0 | 1 | 1 |
| 4551 | 6/27 | 4.4 | No | 0 | 0 | 0 | 0 |
| 4805 | 7/1 | 4.4 | No | 1 | 1 | 0 | 0 |
| 4817 | 8/10 | 5.5 | Yes | 0 | 0 | 2 | 0 |
| 4804 | 7/5 | 6.4 | No | 1 | 1 | 0 | 0 |
| 4560 | 8/13 | 6.5 | Yes | 1 | 1 | 0 | 2 |
| 4839 | 8/15 | 6.5 | Yes | 0 | 0 | 1 | 1 |
| 4816 | 8/9 | 9.5 | Yes | 1 | 1 | 2 | 0 |
| 4840 | 10/6 | 9.7 | Yes | Absent | 1 | Absent | 3 |
| 4564 | 6/30 | 11.4 | No | 0 | 1 | 0 | 0 |
| 4557 | 6/14 | 13.4 | Yes | 1 | 1 | 0 | 2 |
| 4550 | 7/21 | 16.5 | Yes | 1 | 1 | 2 | 0 |
| 4600 | 7/14 | 20.5 | Yes | 1 | 1 | 1 | 1 |

[a]Age based on counts of cementum rings.

4.4-year-old female exhibited neither placental scars nor corpora lutea. The ovaries of the latter did, however, contain mature follicles and she was in estrus. As she was collected at the peak of the breeding season, it is quite possible that she might have successfully bred had she lived. Presence of corpora lutea in a bear 5 ½ years old (Bear No. 4817) and another 6 ½ years old (Bear No. 4839) with no placental scars present to indicate previous pregnancies, may indicate that successful reproduction can be delayed beyond 4 ½ years of age. It is possible, however, that scars from previous pregnancies may have disappeared. Whether this late breeding resulted from a lack of mating or sexual immaturity is not known. Bear No. 4591 was collected on 16 June, and

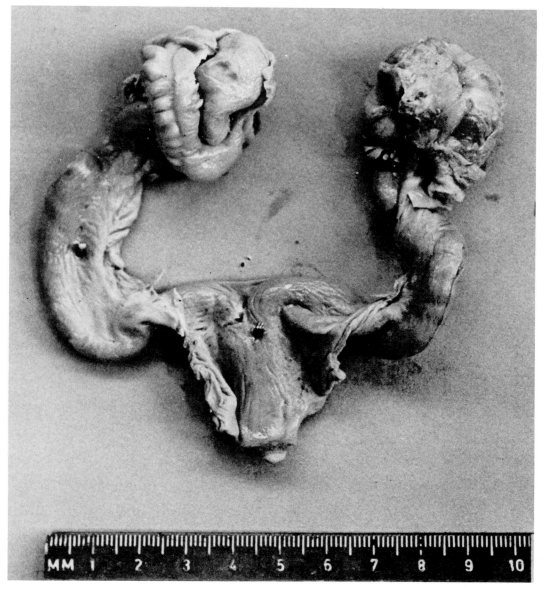

**FIG. 30A.—Reproductive tract of female black bear.**

thus is the earliest instance of corpora lutea development so far recorded. The earliest Erickson and Nellor (1964) observed corpora lutea formation was 20 July. Corpora lutea counts obtained from 11 ovary pairs gave a mean ovulation incidence of 1.9. This is slightly higher than that of 1.8 shown by Jonkel and Cowan (1971) in Montana, but is considerably below the 2.42 shown by Erickson and Nellor (1964) in Michigan. Counts from 8 complete reproductive

83

tracts gave a mean placental scar rate of 1.88, compared to that of 2.85 in Michigan. Examination of the reproductive tracts of 26 bear estimated to be 2 years old or older, gave the same mean incidence of ovulation and placental scars as did the 24 known-age bear.

Multiple ovulations were most often confined to a single ovary (Table 28). Implantations, however, were distributed between both uterine horns,

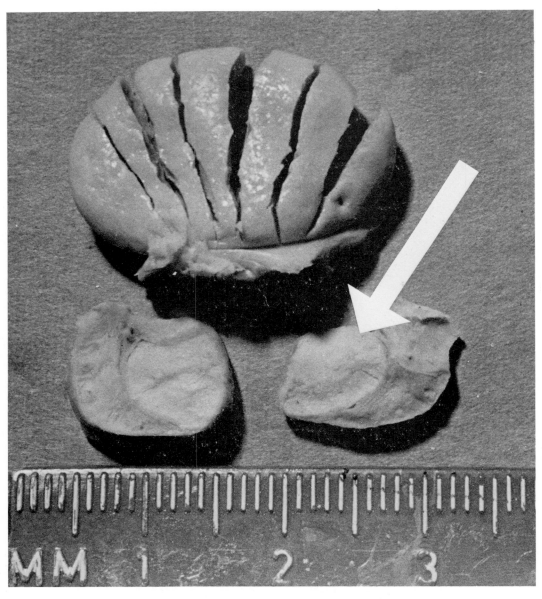

FIG. 30B.—Sectioned black bear ovary. Light area at arrow in excised portion of ovary is corpora lutea.

suggesting migration of embryos from one horn to another. Similar observations were reported by Erickson and Nellor (1964). Presence of recent placental scars in a bear 20 ½ years old (Bear No. 4600) shows that successful reproduction is possible at least to 19 years of age in the wild. The fact that she had developed corpora lutea indicated she was pregnant, and barring adversity, would have produced cubs at 21 ½ years of age. A female, subsequently determined by cementum layers to be 26 years old, was observed to be in estrus in 1965. When collected in 1966, no cubs were present. Unfortunately no reproductive tract was collected from this specimen. This is the oldest bear with which any degree of reproductive activity can be associated from this study. The data on these older bear are offered cautiously as errors of up to 4 years may be made on age-classes determined by cementum layer counts (Guenther 1967).

Reference to Table 27 shows that of 378 females examined, 16 percent were lactating. A separate sample of 1,012 bear, all age classes and both sexes, showed a population with 52 percent females and 48 percent males. (See Population Characteristics for a discussion on sex ratios.) If we were to ignore any bias in these data introduced by differing susceptibility to capture

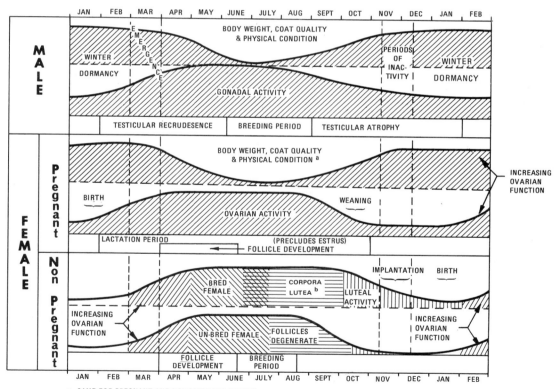

a. SAME FOR PREGNANT AND NON-PREGNANT FEMALE.
b. OVULATION INDUCED BY BREEDING NECESSARY PRECURSER TO CORPORA LUTEA FORMATION.

FIG. 31. - - Seasonal activities, functions and general physical status of black bear in Washington.

on the basis of sex or capture method, we could project a total population of 727 bear for the one from which the 378 females were taken. The total number of females lactating in this population is 59, or only 8.1 percent of the total population. This is a conservative figure as male bear, which will be shown later, are more susceptible to capture during control operations and thus a greater percentage of males are captured than are females.

By combining information obtained during this study, and that from published literature, a general sequence of seasonal activities, such as changes in body weight, variations in coat quality and general physical condition, together with reproductive functions, can be established. Schematic representation of these activities is given in Figure 31.

# PHYSICAL CHARACTERISTICS

Records of several physical characteristics of black bear were kept by field personnel during all phases of the study. One of the objectives of these records was to establish some reliable method by which bear could be accurately aged by field personnel. Body weight, body length, tooth and skull measurements and coat color are some of the characteristics for which records were kept. While most of these proved inadequate for accurate age determinations they do provide useful information pertaining to black bear.

## ANATOMICAL MEASUREMENTS

Most black bear specimens collected during the study were assigned to age categories by field personnel on the basis of tooth wear, weight, body length or a combination of these criteria. One study, however, done in cooperation with project personnel by Keith Guenther, a graduate student of the University of Idaho, Moscow, Idaho, ascribed ages to black bear based on the counting of cementum layers in the canine or premolar tooth (Figs. 32 and 33). Previous investigators have shown the usefulness of this technique in aging black bear (Sauer 1965; Marks and Erickson 1966; Stoneburg and Jonkel 1966; Thomas 1967). Anatomical data from Guenther's study, being directly associated with known-age bear as determined by cementum layers, is reported separately herein from data concerning bear to which an estimated age has been ascribed by field personnel.

### Measurement of Known-age Black Bear

One hundred and seventeen black bear were collected from Grays Harbor and North Olympic Peninsula damage control areas, established by the Washington Forest Protection Association, and the non-damage study area (Fig. 6). Twenty-eight body and skull characteristics, including seven cranial sutures, were studied as possible aides in determining sex and age of black

FIG. 32.—Tooth cementum layers in bear determined to be 6-years-old.

bear. Although much of the data did show definite age groupings and sexual differences, only gross canine size of adult canines was statistically different at the 5 percent level. As this collection of 117 black bear from one population was not large enough for statistically accurate stratification, only selected data, considered useful to field personnel, are presented here. Complete data are

FIG. 33.—Tooth cementum layers in bear determined to be 10-years-old.

available in P-R Job Completion Report, W-71-R-4, Job No. 2, Black Bear
Study, dated January 1, 1967 through June 30, 1967, or in M.S. Thesis, University of Idaho, 73 pp., "Anatomical variations of western Washington black
bear related to age and sex," both by Keith Guenther.

Primary objectives of the study were to develop techniques based on anatomical characteristics by which field personnel could easily and accurately
ascribe age and sex to black bear. In all, six body measurements, nine skull
measurements, weight and length of bacula (penile bone), canine eruption,
wear and root closure, incisor wear, and seven cranial sutures were studied.
Six age classes were used: cub, 1, 2, 3, 4, and over 5 years.

By combining all bear collected in the various areas, a sample of at least five specimens was obtained for each sex and age class, except male cubs, female cubs, female 2- and female 3-year olds.

The male population was better represented than the female. This preponderance of males is partially the result of using foot snares to capture the bear. Male black bear have a much larger occupied area than females (see previous discussion on movements). Wide ranging males therefore have more opportunities to be exposed to a snare.

Bear come to baited snare sets more readily in the spring prior to the onset of berries and other preferred foods. The mean collection date for each age class thus fell during the first part of July, although specimens were collected during each month from April through November.

With the mean collection date occurring in July, class marks separating age classes could be interpreted as occurring in January, the period of winter dormancy. Class marks used in the graphical figures were determined by using the weighted means of adjacent age groups. Starting points of each figure were the mean measurement of the cub group. Seven was the mid-point used for the 5-plus male groups as the median age of the sample was 6.5 and the average age was 7.6. For the female 5-plus age group, 9.0 was used as the mid-point as the average age was 8.5 and the median age was 9.5.

For all age and sex categories, the number, mean, standard deviation and coefficient of variation were first calculated. Sexes were segregated and correlation coefficients were calculated for six separate characteristics that had low coefficients of variation. All characteristics were correlated with age, but differences were not sufficient to be able to separate adjacent age groups statistically at the 5 percent level.

## Weight

Whole weight was taken whenever possible. Field-dressed weights were adjusted to whole weights using the 16 percent weight loss figure determined by Jonkel (1964). Data in Table 29 and Figure 34 show a steady mean weight gain with age. Large standard deviations were partially a result of different seasons of capture, but 3-year-old males caught in June weighed from 68 to 165 pounds and one 3-year-old taken in September weighed 358 pounds. Male cubs taken in September ranged from 18 to 60 pounds.

TABLE 29.—Weight in pounds; with mean, standard deviation and sample size for western Washington black bear according to age and sex.

| MALES | | | | FEMALES | | | |
|---|---|---|---|---|---|---|---|
| Age | Mean | S. D. | No. | Age | Mean | S. D. | No. |
| cub | 20.3 | . . . . | 4 | cub | 16.0 | . . . . | 2 |
| 1 | 74.7 | . . . . | 3 | 1 | 36.3 | . . . . | 6 |
| 2 | 93.8 | 26.96 | 12 | 2 | 49.7 | . . . . | 3 |
| 3 | 170.5 | 98.72 | 6 | 3 | 108.8 | 41.29 | 5 |
| 4 | 195.0 | . . . . | 2 | 4 | 99.0 | . . . . | 2 |
| 5+ | 220.6 | 86.62 | 10 | 5+ | 142.4 | 27.70 | 10 |
| Total observations | | | 37 | Total observations | | | 28 |

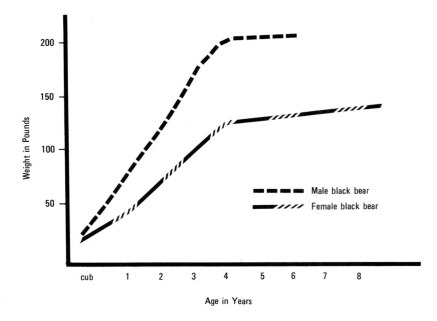

FIG. 34. - - Weight increase related to age and sex of western Washington black bear.

Comparison of weight data between this study and previous ones is difficult, as in all studies, weight data has high standard deviations. Mean weights
for western Washington bear were 10 to 50 percent less than data given for
Michigan bear (Marks and Erickson 1966) and New York bear (Sauer
1966a). When summer weight gains are considered, the difference becomes
less and may, in fact, not exist.

Weight was not a good indicator of age or sex; influence of available
local food supplies evidently overshadows most hereditary weight characteristics.

### Pad Measurement

Width and length of the right hind foot pad were recorded at the widest
and longest parts of the pad. As the rate of increase in both measurements was
proportional, the two were added together to help reduce small measuring errors. Sex and age relationships shown by these measurements are in Table 30.

Sexual dimorphism is noted in maximum pad size attainable. No female
collected had a combined length plus width pad value equal to 10 inches,
whereas 86 percent of the males, 4 years or older, were equal to or greater
than 10 inches combined.

### Zygomatic Width

Zygomatic width was taken at the widest portion of the zygomatic arches
perpendicular to the long axis of the skull. Increase of skull width correlated
well with age (Table 31). Mundy and Fuller (1964) found that the correlation

90

between the determined age and zygomatic width of grizzly bear was "surprisingly good" (r = 0.923, p = 0.001). In this study, correlation of age to zygomatic width was made separately for males (r = 0.92048) and females (r = 0.88439).

TABLE 30.—Track size (right hind pad length plus width) correlated with age-class by sex for western Washington black bear.

| Track size (pad length plus width) | Age-class |
|---|---|
| **Male** | |
| < 7 inches | 100% cubs |
| ≥ 7 inches but < 8 inches | 100% yearlings |
| ≥ 8 inches but < 10 inches | 90% sub-adults (2-3 years) |
| ≥ 10 inches | 80% adults (4 years and over) |
| **Female** | |
| < 6 inches | 100% cubs |
| ≥ 6 inches but < 7 inches | 100% yearlings |
| ≥ 7 inches but < 8.4 inches | 50% sub-adults (2-3 years) |
| ≥ 8.4 inches | 70% adults (4 years and over) |

Increase of zygomatic width as related to age is shown in Figure 35.

TABLE 31.—Zygomatic width in millimeters; with mean, standard deviation and sample size for western Washington black bear according to age and sex.

| MALES | | | | FEMALES | | | |
|---|---|---|---|---|---|---|---|
| Age | Mean | S. D. | No. | Age | Mean | S. D. | No. |
| cub | 92.5 | .... | 4 | cub | 90.0 | .... | 1 |
| 1 | 119.8 | 5.42 | 6 | 1 | 112.5 | 7.54 | 8 |
| 2 | 132.6 | 7.16 | 14 | 2 | 134.0 | .... | 2 |
| 3 | 146.1 | 10.60 | 17 | 3 | 137.7 | 6.52 | 10 |
| 4 | 164.4 | 6.23 | 5 | 4 | 138.5 | .... | 2 |
| 5+ | 175.1 | 15.28 | 10 | 5+ | 152.0 | 6.35 | 15 |
| Total observations | | | 56 | Total observations | | | 38 |

Equations for the regression of age on zygomatic width are:

Males: Log of zygomatic width $= 1.99675 + (0.26511)$ [Log (age) + 1)]

Females: Log of zygomatic width $= 2.01536 + (0.17562)$ [Log (age) + 1)]

Of 108 western Washington black bear skulls that had zygomatic arches intact, 97 (90 percent) were aged according to the following measurements:

Less than 100 mm . . . . . . . . . . . . . . . . . . . . . . . . . . cubs
100-122 mm . . . . . . . . . . . . . . . . . . . . . . . . . yearlings
123-137mm . . . . . . . . . . . . . . . . . . . . . . two-year-olds
138-153 mm . . . . . . . . . . . . . . . . . . three years or older
153 mm and over. . . . . . . . . . . . . . males four years or older

Zygomatic width increases at a relatively constant rate until adulthood is approached. Males averaged slightly more than females in each age category up to 3 years old. After three, most females appear to gain little additional width of the skull. After 3 years zygomatic width in males continues to increase, but at a decreased rate, making additional age categories less precise.

Of bear aged incorrectly, one yearling and one 2-year-old were over-aged one year. Nine specimens were 3-year-olds, and all were under-aged. Although the divisions used for zygomatic width age classes gave the highest accuracy possible with this sample, further investigations may indicate a better division between 2- and 3-year-old categories.

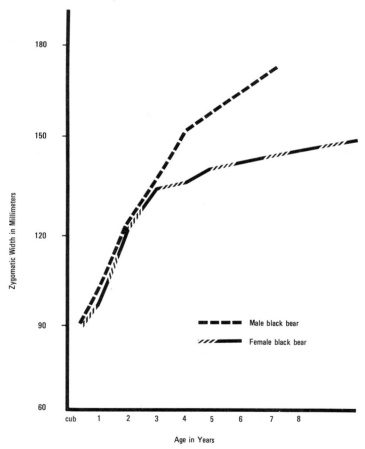

FIG. 35. - - Zygomatic width increase with age for western Washington black bear.

An attempt was made to duplicate the zygomatic measurement plus the thickness of the skin covering the zygomatic process of the temporal bone. Of the bear collected, 67 cheek widths were measured before cleaning, and corresponding zygomatic widths measured after cleaning. Relationship between cheek width and zygomatic width is shown in Figure 36. The difference is primarily a function of thickness of the skin overlying the zygomatic processes of the temporal and malar bones. Muscle or cartilage present, is about 2 mm for cubs, 4 to 5 mm for yearlings, and 8 to 13 mm for adults. Differences are noted in Fig. 36 and Table 32.

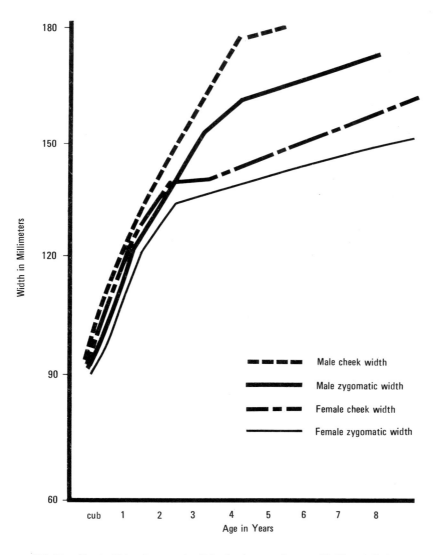

FIG. 36. - - Cheek width and zygomatic width related to age of western Washington black bear.

93

TABLE 32.—**Cheek width in millimeters; with mean, standard deviation, and sample size for western Washington black bear according to age and sex.**

| MALES | | | | FEMALES | | | |
|---|---|---|---|---|---|---|---|
| Age | Mean | S. D. | No. | Age | Mean | S. D. | No. |
| cub | 93.5 | . . . . | 2 | cub | 91.0 | . . . . | 2 |
| 1 | 122.5 | . . . . | 4 | 1 | 115.4 | 8.12 | 7 |
| 2 | 138.7 | 8.53 | 14 | 2 | 136.3 | . . . . | 3 |
| 3 | 154.6 | 12.62 | 16 | 3 | 144.0 | 8.44 | 6 |
| 4 | 175.0 | . . . . | 2 | 4 | 138.0 | . . . . | 1 |
| 5+ | 180.5 | . . . . | 3 | 5+ | 160.9 | 4.88 | 7 |
| Total observations | | | 41 | Total observations | | | 26 |

Correlations of cheek width to age were: males, $r = .86991$, and females, $r = .90211$. Respective equations were:

Males: Log cheek width $= 1.99654 + (.30819) [\text{Log(age} + 1)]$

Females: Log cheek width $= 2.00331 + (.22023) [\text{Log(age} + 1)]$

Cheek width is both easy to use and fairly accurate in the field up to about 3 years of age for females and 4 years of age for males. The close relationship found between zygomatic arch width and cheek width will enable investigators who already have a collection of skulls from a particular area to determine cheek width age groups that can be used in the field, as previously suggested by Mundy and Fuller (1964).

Limits for age groups presented are probably true only for coastal areas of western Washington, as bear taken from mountainous areas of northeast Washington, *U. a. cinnamomum* (an admittedly small sample of seven), averaged 5 to 10 percent below the means for western Washington bear of the same age and sex.

### Bacula Characteristics

Mean bacula weights recorded to the nearest tenth of a gram for six age classes are shown in Table 33.

TABLE 33.—**Baculum weight in grams; with mean, standard deviation and sample size for western Washington black bear according to age.**

| Age | Mean | S. D. | No. |
|---|---|---|---|
| cub | 0.3 | . . . . | 1 |
| 1 | 1.4 | . . . . | 2 |
| 2 | 3.6 | 0.92 | 13 |
| 3 | 5.6 | 3.60 | 7 |
| 4 | 7.1 | . . . . | 2 |
| 5+ | 10.4 | 2.28 | 6 |
| Total observations | | | 31 |

Stickley (1957) studied bacula of 17 black bear collected in Virginia. Lack of accompanying skeletal material prevented Stickley from aging bear in his collection, but with predominantly old bear he found, "The adult baculasic is much longer and thicker, especially at the proximal end, whereas the immature (102 to 125 pounds) bone is short and spindley." Erickson and Nellor (1964) with 8 known-age black bear bacula, and Mark and Erickson (1966) with 14 known-age black bear bacula, both concluded that the size of the baculum appeared to be correlated closely with age.

Size of bacula collected in this study, were highly correlated with age (weight-- r = .83315, length-- r = .84419). Again, however, the difference between age groups was not sufficiently great to be used as a statistically accurate aging technique. A comparison of bacula weights given by Marks and Erickson (1966) for Michigan black bear, and bacula weights obtained for black bear from western Washington is shown in Figure 37. The oldest bear studied was 7½ years old, making it impossible to project beyond this age. Marks and Erickson (1966), felt their data suggested ". . . that the baculum grows continually throughout the life of the individual."

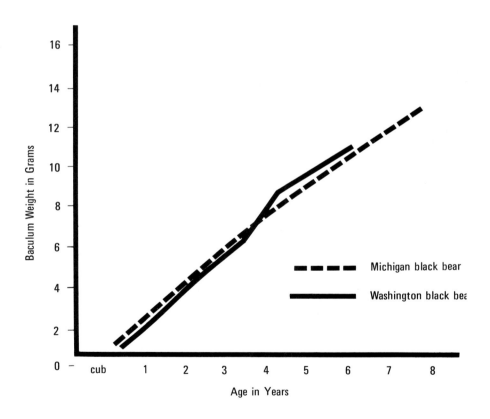

FIG. 37. - - Baculum weight of Washington black bear and Michigan black bear (from Marks and Erickson 1966) related to age.

Rate of baculum weight increase is comparable, with Michigan bear having somewhat heavier bacula in the younger age groups. Data obtained by Erickson and Nellor (1964) indicated larger means, but his were killed primarily in the fall. The range for Michigan's 2 to 4 year old bear was 3.2 to 11.6 grams for 22 bacula. Bacula in this collection had a greater range for 3-year-olds (1.9 to 12.3 grams) with only seven specimens.

Both studies showed fairly definite age groupings for cubs and yearlings. The sub-adult class (2- and 3-year-olds) had a wide range. A portion of the variation might be explained if some bear mature earlier than others, perhaps because of better feed in some areas. If the premise that some males become sexually mature in their third year, while others do not, is true, then the high standard deviations for the 3-year-olds might be expected.

Bacula length was also recorded for 31 bear from western Washington (Table 34). Rate of length increase appeared to slow after 4 years of age. A

TABLE 34.—Baculum length in millimeters; with mean, standard deviation and sample size for western Washington black bear according to age.

| Age | Mean | S. D. | No. |
|-----|------|-------|-----|
| cub | 39 | . . . . | 1 |
| 1 | 71 | . . . . | 2 |
| 2 | 104 | 7.86 | 13 |
| 3 | 115 | 18.99 | 7 |
| 4 | 131 | . . . . | 2 |
| 5+ | 140 | 9.62 | 6 |
| Total observations | | | 31 |

comparison with Michigan data is given in Figure 38. Bacula lengths of Washington bear are considerably smaller than those given for Michigan by Marks and Erickson (1966).

Washington bear would be under-aged about one year if age class divisions for Michigan were used for Washington bear.

*Canine Root Opening*

The pulp canal opening at the apex of the root was recorded to the nearest millimeter.

Marks and Erickson (1966) noted of root closure that: "The apex of the root canal was barely open in the canine of a captive specimen aged 3 years, 11 months. . . . The pulp cavity was closed in two female captives, aged 4 years, 5 months . . . and 5 years, 6 months . . ."

Sauer and Free (1965) used gross appearance of the canines to separate bear into age classes as follows: "The canine root of bear 3½ to 5½ years old was closed, but the pith cavity remained open."

The relationship of the size of the root canal opening of the lower right canine to age by sex for 97 black bear collected in the coastal zone of western

Washington is shown in Figure 39. Data collected from Washington appear to correlate closely with that of Sauer and Free (1965) for New York bear.

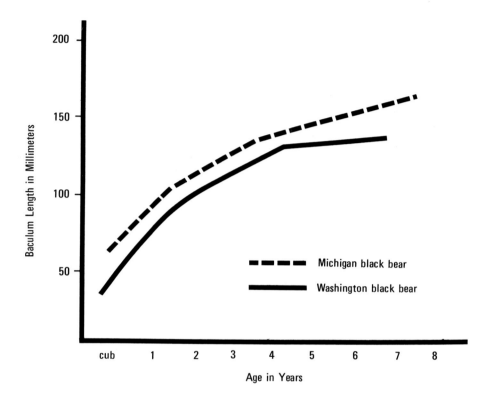

FIG. 38. - - Baculum length of Washington black bear and Michigan black bear (from Marks and Erickson 1966) related to age.

A definite closure rate was noted which can be used to separate bear into the following age categories: males 1, 2, 3 and 4 years; females 1, 2 and 3 years. When the 97 bear were aged according to root closure, all but 3 were aged correctly. These were all 3-year-old males that had canines with closed roots.

When using these data for aging it is important to note that the mean collection date was the first week of July, and since many hunter-killed bear are taken in the fall, a different set of parameters might be needed.

Data presented in Table 35 show that a definite difference does occur in the size of the root opening between males and females of the same age, and that separate categories are needed for each sex.

97

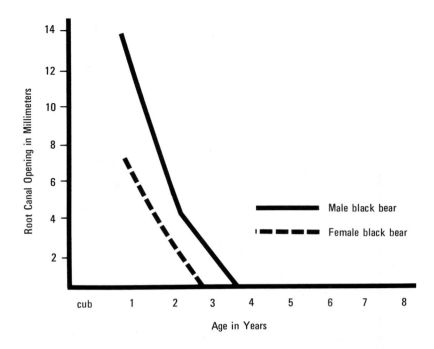

FIG. 39. - - Canine root canal opening related to age and sex of black bear from western Washington.

Sauer and Free (1965) found the canine root opening closed in 3½-year-old bear. The sample of western Washington bear showed that the 10, 3½-year-old females had closed canine root openings, but that 14 of 17, 3½-year-old males had open roots. Male 3-year-olds with closed roots were much larger than average and appeared to be older in all respects, except the count of cementum layers.

TABLE 35.—Canine root opening in millimeters; with mean, standard deviation and sample size for western Washington black bear according to age and sex.

| | MALES | | | | FEMALES | | |
|---|---|---|---|---|---|---|---|
| Age | Mean | S. D. | No. | Age | Mean | S. D. | No. |
| cub | . . . . | . . . . | . . | cub | . . . . | . . . . | . . |
| 1 | 13.7 | 1.51 | 6 | 1 | 7.6 | 1.85 | 8 |
| 2 | 6.2 | 1.24 | 17 | 2 | 3.5 | . . . . | 4 |
| 3 | 2.8 | 1.91 | 17 | 3 | 0.0 | 0.00 | 10 |
| 4 | 0.0 | 0.00 | 5 | 4 | 0.0 | 0.00 | 3 |
| 5+ | 0.0 | 0.00 | 11 | 5+ | 0.0 | 0.00 | 16 |
| Total observations | | | 56 | Total observations | | | 41 |

### Canine Root Length

The lower right canine maximum root length was measured from the apex of the root to the dentino-enamel junction on the anterior edge of the tooth (Table 36). Specimens that had considerable wear on the enamel portion were not able to be measured accurately and if the original dentino-enamel junction was not evident, the base of the root to the gum line was considered the root of the tooth.

**TABLE 36.—Canine root length (lower) in millimeters; with mean, standard deviation and sample size for western Washington black bear according to age and sex.**

| | MALES | | | | FEMALES | | |
|---|---|---|---|---|---|---|---|
| Age | Mean | S. D. | No. | Age | Mean | S. D. | No. |
| cub | . . . . | . . . . | . . | cub | . . . . | . . . . | . . |
| 1 | 39.0 | 3.85 | 6 | 1 | 36.3 | 3.85 | 8 |
| 2 | 48.8 | 2.74 | 17 | 2 | 41.5 | . . . . | 4 |
| 3 | 49.8 | 3.87 | 17 | 3 | 43.7 | 2.31 | 10 |
| 4 | 54.4 | 2.19 | 5 | 4 | 43.0 | . . . . | 3 |
| 5+ | 53.3 | 3.35 | 11 | 5+ | 43.5 | 3.18 | 15 |
| Total observations | | | 56 | Total observations | | | 40 |

The root length was taken instead of total length, as old bear with broken teeth cannot have the total length measured, whereas tooth wear or breakage does not affect the length of the root.

A significant difference by the one-tailed t-test (P = .05) was found between sexes for the mean canine root lengths for canines with closed roots. Marks and Erickson (1966) found a significant difference between the sexes for upper mean canine tooth measurements for Michigan bear: total length, greatest diameter and transverse diameter. Sauer (1966b) noted that sex could be accurately determined by gross size of lower canines.

Root length could not be used by itself to determine age.

### Canine Eruption

Canines continue to erupt slowly for at least 4 or 5 years. The degree of eruption was used to age bear if the lower canine root canal was closed or it was not desirable to extract the canines. Sexual differences were not noticeable. Generally when no dentine was exposed above the alveolar fossae, the bear were yearlings. Bear were at least three years old if any portion of the dentino-enamel junction was visible above the gum line. Bear were usually at least five years old if the dentino-enamel junction was entirely above the gum line. All specimens with the dentino-enamel junction more than 5 mm above the gum line were at least 10 years old.

### Measurements of Estimated-age Black Bear

Anatomical measurements were obtained from black bear collected in four damage control areas of western Washington established by the Washington Forest Protection Association and the non-damage study area. Animals were assigned to age classes on the basis of gross physical characteristics, primarily relative size. Age class criterion were cub (less than 12 months), yearling (12-23 months), sub-adult (23-47 months) and adult (48 months or more). Most age assignments were made by bear control personnel. Some characteristics were measured on as many as 888 bear. Of this sample, 117 were subsequently aged by cementum layer counts. These animals were discussed above. Mean values for nine anatomical characteristics measured, by age class and sex, are given in Table 37.

**TABLE 37.—Mean values for nine anatomical measurements of western Washington black bear by estimated age-class and sex.**

| Anatomical feature | Age-class | | | |
|---|---|---|---|---|
| | Cub | Yearling | Subadult | Adult |
| | . . . . . . . . . . . . . . . . . . . **pounds** . . . . . . . . . . . . . . . . | | | |
| Body weight | 25/32[a] | 67/58 | 115/91 | 216/134 |
| | . . . . . . . . . . . . . . . . . . . **inches** . . . . . . . . . . . . . . . . . | | | |
| Body length (nose tip to base of tail) | 31/31 | 45/43 | 52/49 | 61/53 |
| Neck circumference | 12/11 | 15/15 | 18/17 | 25/20 |
| Girth (behind shoulder) | 17/19 | 25/23 | 30/28 | 38/32 |
| Ulna length | 6.5/6.4 | 8.9/8.8 | 10.4/9.8 | 12.5/10.7 |
| Tibia length | 7.4/7.7 | 9.8/9.7 | 11.5/11.1 | 12.9/11.7 |
| Rear pad length | 3.2/3.2 | 4.3/4.0 | 4.9/4.4 | 5.6/4.8 |
| Rear pad width | 2.3/2.6 | 3.1/2.9 | 3.6/3.2 | 4.1/3.6 |
| Upper canine length | .52/.50 | .88/.85 | .96/.93 | 1.10/.97 |

[a]Mean value for male/mean value for female.

## Weight and Length

Weight and body length of nine bear, five from the damage study area and four from the non-damage study area, taken at least one year apart, are shown in Figure 40. Body length was measured from the tip of the nose to the base of the tail, with the bear in a natural position on its side. Annual increments of weight and body length are based on measurements taken at the same time each year. The single cub gained 27 pounds between October 1966 and October 1967. Three yearlings gained an average of 35 pounds during their second year of life. One yearling male gained an average of .98 pounds per day in a 53-day mid-summer period. This compares with a .84 pound per day weight increment reported by Jonkel and Cowan (1971) for 14 Montana bear over a 30-day period and one adult female gaining 1.55 pounds per day over a 22-day period. Annual body length increment for younger bear ranged from 5 to 9 inches.

One hypothesis concerning the cause of bear damage is that food stress might cause bear to use less desirable food items such as sapwood. If this hypothesis were to prove true, one might suspect that bear from damage areas might differ physically from bear in non-damage areas where food is supposedly more abundant. Two of these physical differences might be weight and body length. Bear under food stress would be expected to weigh less and have

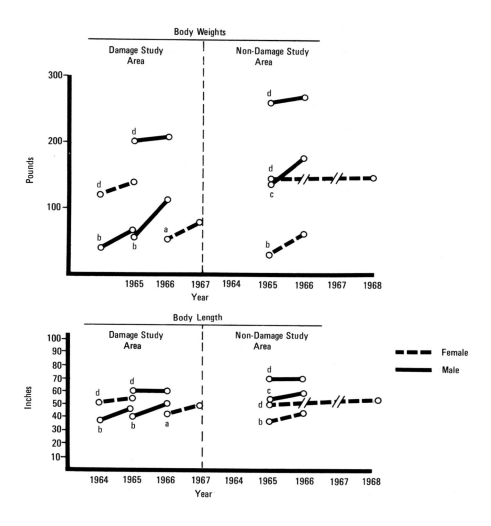

<sup>a</sup>Cub at first measurement
<sup>b</sup>Yearling at first measurement
<sup>c</sup>Subadult at first measurement
<sup>d</sup>Adult at first measurement

FIG. 40. - - Annual weights and body lengths for five black bear from the damage
and four from the non-damage study area, Grays Harbor County, Washington.
Measurements for each individual bear taken in same month each year.

a shorter body length than comparable bear not under food stress. No such
differences were found in this small sample.

Weights and body measurements of 29 cubs collected in western Washington, 10 of which were twin litter mates, are given in Table 38.

A pair of abandoned newborn cubs, a male and a female, were collected
from a den February 3, 1970. Each measured 14.5 inches in body length and
was covered with short, dense black hair (Fig. 41). The male weighed 1.9 and

**TABLE 38.—Body weight and length of 29 western Washington black bear cubs.**

| Collection Month/Day | Sex | Weight (pounds) | Length (inches) |
|---|---|---|---|
| 6/19 | M | 16 | 30 |
| 6/29 | M | 28 | 30 |
| 7/2 | M | 16 | 27 |
| 7/2 | M[a] | 14 | 25 |
| 7/6 | M[a] | 16 | 27 |
| 7/5 | M | 26 | 31 |
| 7/7 | M | 25 | 29 |
| 7/13 | M[a] | 17 | 27 |
| 7/13 | F[a] | 18 | 28 |
| 7/17 | F | 17 | 29 |
| 7/21 | M[a] | 18 | 22 |
| 7/26 | M[a] | 16 | 24 |
| Mean values (June & July) | | 18.9 | 27.4 |
| 8/4 | F | 15 | 26 |
| 8/8 | M | 24 | 38 |
| 8/10 | M | 42 | 33 |
| 8/26 | M[a] | 19 | 32 |
| 8/26 | M[a] | 16 | 28 |
| 8/31 | M | 19 | 30 |
| 9/4 | F | 27 | 30 |
| 9/6 | F | 52 | 36 |
| 9/10 | F | 28 | 33 |
| 9/19 | F | 24 | 30 |
| 9/26 | M | 30 | 37 |
| 9/28 | M | 35 | 39 |
| 9/30 | F | 38 | 30 |
| 10/3 | F | 17 | 29 |
| 10/3 | M | 66 | 42 |
| 10/5 | F | 37 | 36 |
| 10/5 | F | 51 | 42 |
| Mean Values (August-October) | | 31.7 | 33.5 |

[a]Litter mates.

the female 1.8 pounds. Estimated time of parturition was mid-January. Weights of 29 cubs collected between mid-June and early October ranged from 14 to 66 pounds. During this period 18 males averaged 24.6 pounds, and 11 females 29.5 pounds. The greater mean weight for females is the result of a greater proportion of females being collected later in the summer. Cubs of both sexes are apparently comparable in weight and body length at a given time during their first summer. Weights and body measurements of litter mates among the five pairs of cubs were similar. Cubs from different litters, however, varied widely in weight and size. As shown in Table 38, 12 cubs collected from mid-June through July averaged 18.9 pounds in weight and 27.4 inches in length. Seventeen cubs collected between August and early October averaged 31.7 pounds in weight and 33.5 inches in body length. Five of the late season cub weights were notably smaller than average, weighing only 15.0

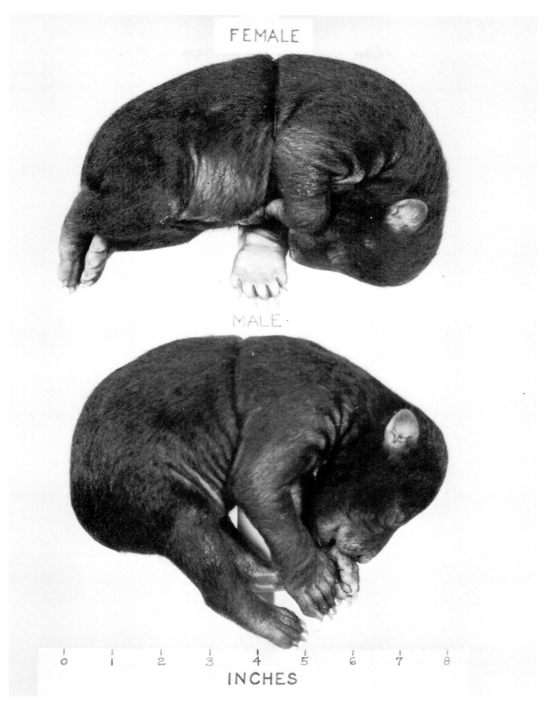

FEMALE

MALE

0  1  2  3  4  5  6  7  8
INCHES

FIG. 41.—Pair of recently born, abandoned cubs collected from winter den on February 3, 1970, in western Washington. Male weight: **1.9 pounds**; female weight: **1.8 pounds**.

to 18.5 pounds. No correlation of differences in weight and size of cubs at specific periods of time to separation from family groups or to different areas of origin was noted. Ten small cubs weighing 14 to 18.5 pounds were known to be with their mothers when collected.

Body weight and length for 664 and 872 black bear respectively, from four damage areas in western Washington and the Grays Harbor non-damage study area, are given in Figures 42 and 43. Measurements were taken primarily by bear control personnel. Because of wide disparities in total bear captured between damage and non-damage areas and widely varying sex ratios resulting from several uncontrolled variables, no differentiation by sex is shown. Differences in sample sizes and total area sampled preclude drawing any valid inferences from this data on a damage area versus non-damage area basis. A 444 pound male and a 246 pound female were the heaviest specimens of each sex recorded.

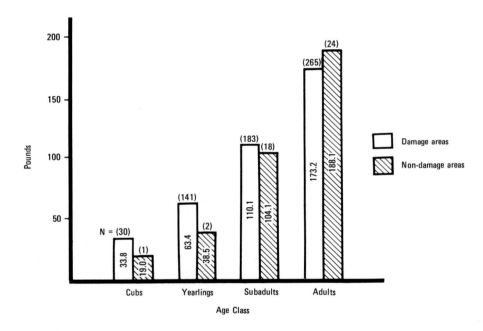

FIG. 42. - - Mean body weight of 664 western Washington black bear by age class, sexes combined, damage and non-damage areas compared.

## GROSS PHYSICAL APPEARANCE

Evaluations of physical condition and coat condition were made on 817 and 407 black bear from damage and non-damage areas respectively, during the period 1964 through 1966. Physical condition was determined as "poor" for bear that were thin and "good" for bear that were average or above average in weight for their age class. Coat quality was determined also as "poor"

104

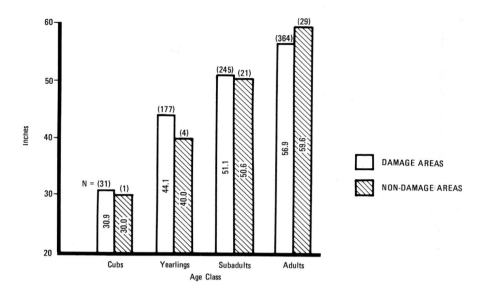

FIG. 43. - - Mean body length of 872 western Washington black bear by age class, sexes combined, damage and non-damage areas compared.

or "good" based on broad criteria of glossiness, absence of bare spots, thickness and overall appearance. These subjective classifications in most cases were made by bear control personnel. These personnel had experience obtained from handling hundreds of bear through the years to apply to these classifications.

## Physical Condition

Data in Figure 44 show that black bear decline in general physical condition following emergence. Incidence of black bear in poor physical condition increases from 25 percent in April to a peak of 36 percent in June. General condition improves from this point until denning in late fall when no bear were noted to be in poor condition. Data in Figure 45 show physical condition by age-class in damage and non-damage areas. Again, sample size and total area sampled are so different as to preclude drawing any definite inferences. It appears, however, that yearlings and sub-adults, as a group, are in generally poorer condition than adults throughout the whole area. This was noted as particularly true between the damage and non-damage study areas. No significant difference was apparent between the means of all age groups when compared on a damage to non-damage area basis.

In an attempt to refine evaluations of general physical condition, this evaluation was broadened to include the incidence of fat deposits. Gross field autopsies were performed and the presence or absence of rump, intestinal and kidney fat was recorded. Seasonal fluctuations in these deposits are shown in Figure 46. The general decline in fat deposits coincides with condition evaluations noted previously but is somewhat more objective in approach. The

105

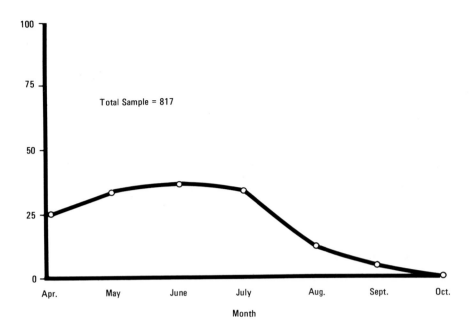

FIG. 44. - - Percentage of western Washington black bear in apparent poor physical condition - 1964 through 1966.

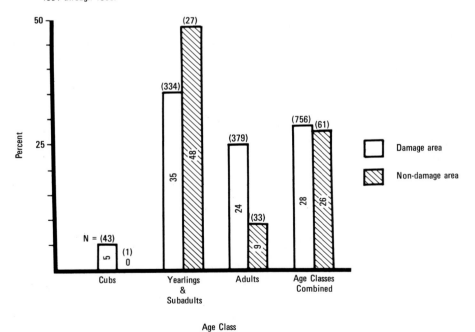

FIG. 45. - -Percent of western Washington black bear in apparent poor physical condition by age-class, damage and non-damage areas - - 1964 through 1966.

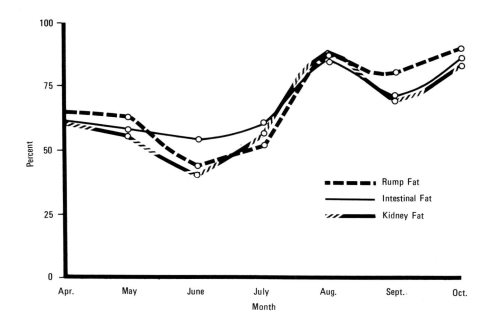

FIG. 46. - - Percent occurrence of fat deposits in western Washington black bear, April through October 1966.

highest incidence of fat deposits occurs, as one would expect, in late fall as the bear prepares to den.

## Coat Condition

Coat condition, while not always an indicator of general physical condition, was recorded for 407 black bear from damage areas in western Washington. Percentage of bear with good coats ranged from 72 percent immediately following emergence in the spring, to a low of 12 percent in July, and back to 71 percent in late fall (Figure 47). This pattern shows the general shedding and growth of the winter coat. A general pattern of poor coat condition immediately prior to denning or upon emergence, might be considered an indication of poor physical condition. For the sportsman interested in obtaining a quality pelt for a trophy, early spring and late fall are obviously the best bet.

## COLOR PHASES

Black bear exist in a wide array of color phases, but the familiar black phase is dominant over the range of the species. Color phases are distributed in regional patterns and populations of different color phases are common in western North America.

A study by Cowan (1938) of fur records of trading posts in the northwest provided extensive data on color phase distribution. Of 19,228 black bear pelts recorded from posts along coastal British Columbia, 7 percent were of

107

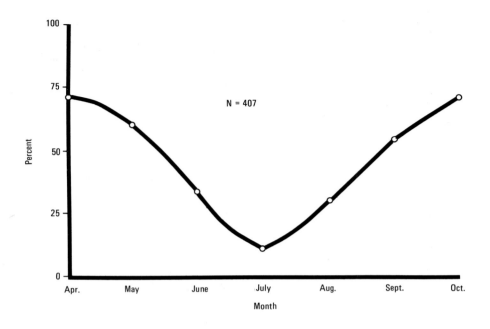

FIG. 47. - - Percent of western Washington black bear with coats in good shape by month - 1966.

the brown color phase. Records at Ft. Vancouver showed 21 percent of the brown phase. This figure was no doubt influenced by pelts brought down the Columbia River from interior areas. An east-west gradient of brown phase incidence was shown when looking at trading post records in the Rocky Mountains where only 37 percent of the black bear were of the black phase. This percentage increased to 100 percent as one moved to the Pacific Coast. A north-south gradient similar to that found along the foothills of the Cascade Mountains in western Washington was found in Idaho where the frequency of black phase bear increased from 37 percent in southern Idaho to 93 percent in what was then New Caledonia.

Color phases recorded among 1,645 black bear collected throughout western Washington from 1963 to 1966 are shown in Table 39. Of 1,054 bear taken from relatively low elevation coastal forests of the Olympic Peninsula and the northeastern part of the Willapa Hills, all, except for a single dark brown adult male, were black. Two of nine bear collected in the southeastern Willapa Hills contiguous with the foothills of the southern Cascade Mountains were of the brown phase.

Both black and brown colored bear were recorded among 582 specimens taken in the western foothills of the southern Cascade Mountains (Thurston County south to Clark County). A high incidence of brown phase bear, 50 percent, was recorded from the upper Cowlitz River drainage; however, the sample included only 8 specimens. The average percentage of brown phase bear for all areas with a mixed black-brown population was 21 percent. While

**TABLE 39.—Color phases recorded for 1,645 black bear in western Washington.**

| General region | Sample size | Percent black phase | Percent brown phase |
|---|---|---|---|
| Coastal— | | | |
|     Olympic Peninsula | 958 | 100 | . . . |
|     NE Willapa Hills | 96 | 100 | . . . |
|     SE Willapa Hills | 9 | 78 | 22 |
| Inland— | | | |
|     Skookumchuck and | | | |
|       Newaukum Rivers | 166 | 88 | 12 |
|     Upper Cowlitz River | 8 | 50 | 50 |
|     Toutle, Green and | | | |
|     Coweeman Rivers | 218 | 82 | 18 |
|     Kalama and Lewis Rivers | 190 | 70 | 30 |

family group members of different color phases are noted elsewhere, no such mixing was observed in western Washington. In the area where both brown and black phases occurred, three adult females of brown color had four cubs, all brown; 10 black females had 15 black cubs, and 2 pair of cubs separated from their mother were all black. One unusual case of a bear that was uniformly brown dorsally (above the lateral mid-line) and uniformly black ventrally (below the lateral mid-line) was noted.

Generally the black and brown color phases in Washington are separated along a north-south line from the U. S.-Canada border to the Columbia River near the western base of the Cascade Mountains. Black bear in eastern Washington are typically a mixture of black and brown phase individuals.

# FOOD HABITS

A knowledge of the food habits of black bear is a necessary prerequisite to an understanding of how they interact with their habitat. While food habit studies performed elsewhere are important to the areas where conducted and contribute to an overall understanding of black bear, comparison of these data from different regions such as Alaska, Pennsylvania, Montana and Washington are of limited value with respect to local food selection and are not presented in this discussion. Readers interested in such regional information are referred to studies by Hatler (1967), Bennett et al. (1943), Tisch (1961) and Spencer (1955). Omnivorous habits of the black bear, plus his opportunistic selection of available food items, indicate that food habit studies done on a local basis are most useful in studying a given population. Three such studies have been done over the years in western Washington. The earliest was conducted by personnel of the Washington State Department of Game in 1952 through 1954 (Brent and Bowhay 1956). This study was done in response to initial concern with the emergence of black bear damage to conifers. Stomach samples were collected from 288 bear taken in control operations on damage areas in Grays Harbor County. A second study was done by a bear control hunter, Bernie Paque, who examined 205 stomachs for major food items only, during 1967 through 1969, in the northern Olympic Peninsula area. The third study was done as part of the Cooperative Black Bear Study in 1968. This study involved a comparison of food habits between the damage and non-damage study areas using both scat and stomach samples. A total of 289 samples were analyzed, 227 scat and 62 stomach. As the areas where these studies were done are different and various investigators using a variety of techniques were involved, no direct, valid comparisons can be drawn. Information from each study will be presented separately. Data from the latest study will be discussed in relation to information on the vegetation survey presented earlier. From these several sources a summary of the food habits of black bear in western Washington will be presented.

## FOOD HABIT STUDIES

### Study I—Grays Harbor County

In the earliest study, 288 stomach samples were collected from black bear taken in the Wynoochee, Wishkah and Humptulips watersheds in Grays Harbor County, Washington.

One-quart samples were taken from each bear and preserved in ten percent formalin. For analysis the material was washed clear in a one-sixteenth inch mesh screen and then floated in water. Individual food particles were identified and placed by species in separate containers. Separate food items were then measured by ocular estimate.

Twenty-nine separate items or categories of items were identified. Percent composition and frequency of each food item is shown in Table 40.

Bird, fish and mammal material, combined as a single category, and insects each comprised 6 percent of the bear's diet, while vegetable material afforded 73 percent. The remaining 15 percent of the diet was debris and other miscellaneous non-food items.

Utilization of food items by month is shown in Table 41. Data in Figure 48 show the trend of the five most important food items. Wood fiber made up approximately 24, 29 and 45 percent of the monthly diet, respectively, in April, May and June, but then declined in July to trace levels in August and September. Skunk cabbage was eaten every month, with its peak of 20 percent in monthly use, based on percent composition of the diet, occurring in April. All parts, leaves, flowering stock and roots were eaten.

Huckleberry (*Vaccinium* spp.), like skunk cabbage, appeared in the diet every month, reaching a low of 0.3 percent in June, and a high of 30 percent

**TABLE 40.—Results of food analysis of 288 black bear stomach samples collected in Grays Harbor County, Washington, in 1952, 1953, and 1954.**

| Food Item[a] | Percent | |
|---|---|---|
| | Frequency | Composition |
| Wood fibers | 18 | 15 |
| Skunk cabbage | 31 | 12 |
| Huckleberry | 37 | 11 |
| Fungus | 25 | 10 |
| Salal | 21 | 8 |
| Cascara | 13 | 6 |
| Devil's club | 12 | 3 |
| False dandelion | 5 | 2 |
| Grasses | 21 | 2 |
| *Rubus* spp. | 11 | 2 |
| Apple | 3 | 1 |
| Evergreen needles | 41 | 0.2 |
| Horsetail | 0.3 | 0.2 |
| *Prunus* spp. | 1 | 0.1 |
| Oso-berry | 0.3 | 0.1 |
| Lichens | 0.3 | T[b] |
| Moss | 0.7 | T |
| Deer fern | 2 | T |
| Bracken fern | 2 | T |
| Oxalis | 0.3 | T |
| Bedstraw | 0.3 | T |
| Alder | 0.7 | T |
| Salmonberry | 0.3 | T |
| Oregon grape | 0.3 | T |
| Elderberry | 0.7 | T |
| Strawberry | 0.3 | T |
| Insects | 35 | 6 |
| Birds, fish & mammals | 12 | 6 |
| Miscellaneous material (Debris, dirt, and unidentified material) | 35 | 15 |

[a]Listed in order of percent composition.
[b]Trace amounts.

in November. Leaves and blossoms of huckleberry were eaten before the fruit set on, as was the vegetative tissue of devil's club and apple.

Other food items consumed every month, along with huckleberry and skunk cabbage, were fungus, grass and evergreen needles. Fungus made up 23 percent of the monthly diet in September, climax of a gradual increase from May, when it occurred as a trace.

Salal was utilized over a five-month period from June through October, reaching a peak of 28 percent in September.

**TABLE 41.—Frequency and composition, by month, of food items used by black bear as determined by analysis of 288 stomach samples collected in Grays Harbor County, Washington, during 1952, 1953 and 1954.**

| Food Item | April Freq % | April Comp % | May Freq % | May Comp % | June Freq % | June Comp % | July Freq % | July Comp % | August Freq % | August Comp % | September Freq % | September Comp % | October Freq % | October Comp % | November Freq % | November Comp % |
|---|---|---|---|---|---|---|---|---|---|---|---|---|---|---|---|---|
| Wood fiber | 33 | 24 | 44 | 29 | 66 | 45 | 9 | 7 | 2 | Tᵃ | 3 | T | 0 | 0 | 0 | 0 |
| Skunk cabbage | 33 | 20 | 33 | 13 | 37 | 6 | 49 | 15 | 41 | 15 | 49 | 8 | 18 | 11 | 20 | 6 |
| Huckleberry | 33 | 5 | 60 | 15 | 23 | .3 | 47 | 18 | 59 | 11 | 42 | 12 | 36 | 3 | 60 | 30 |
| Fungus | 8 | .4 | 5 | T | 3 | 1 | 38 | 7 | 27 | 18 | 58 | 23 | 36 | 20 | 20 | 12 |
| Salal | 0 | 0 | 0 | 0 | 23 | 6 | 11 | .2 | 46 | 13 | 79 | 28 | 18 | .1 | 0 | 0 |
| Cascara | 0 | 0 | 0 | 0 | 0 | 0 | 0 | 0 | 27 | 7 | 55 | 19 | 72 | 45 | 0 | 0 |
| Devil's club | 8 | T | 26 | 6 | 40 | 11 | 16 | 3 | 0 | 0 | 0 | T | 0 | 0 | 0 | 0 |
| False dandelion | 0 | 0 | 9 | 3 | 17 | 9 | 4 | 2 | 4 | .1 | 3 | T | 0 | 0 | 0 | 0 |
| Grasses | 25 | .8 | 44 | 4 | 40 | 4 | 22 | .7 | 9 | 2 | 21 | 2 | 18 | .2 | 11 | 0 |
| Blackberry | 0 | 0 | 9 | T | 6 | T | 18 | 4 | 30 | 7 | 15 | .2 | 5 | 0 | 0 | 0 |
| Apple | 0 | 0 | 2 | .1 | 3 | T | 1 | T | 4 | .1 | 3 | .2 | 18 | 5 | 40 | 40 |
| Evergreen needles | 58 | .8 | 42 | .4 | 57 | T | 47 | .1 | 50 | .2 | 61 | .2 | 64 | 60 | 60 | T |
| Horsetail | 0 | 0 | 2 | .9 | 0 | 0 | 0 | 0 | 2 | .02 | 3 | T | 0 | 0 | 0 | 0 |
| Prunus spp. | 0 | 0 | 0 | .5 | 0 | 0 | 0 | 0 | 0 | 0 | 0 | 0 | 0 | 0 | 0 | 0 |
| Oso-berry | 0 | 0 | 2 | 0 | 0 | 0 | 2 | .4 | 0 | 0 | 0 | 0 | 0 | 0 | 0 | 0 |
| Lichens | 0 | 0 | 0 | 0 | 3 | .1 | 0 | 0 | 0 | .1 | 0 | 0 | 0 | 0 | 0 | 0 |
| Insects | 8 | .8 | 26 | 4 | 24 | 2 | 15 | 15 | 63 | 10 | 15 | 18 | 20 | 0 | 0 | 0 |
| Birds, fish & mammals | 42 | 17 | 16 | 7 | 12 | 4 | 7 | 2 | 9 | 3 | 24 | 7 | 9 | .3 | 20 | 0 |
| Miscellaneous material (debris, dirt, & unidentified) | 33 | 31 | 47 | 17 | 51 | 11 | 69 | 24 | 57 | 14 | 3 | .3 | 27 | 9 | 0 | 0 |

ᵃ T indicated trace amount.

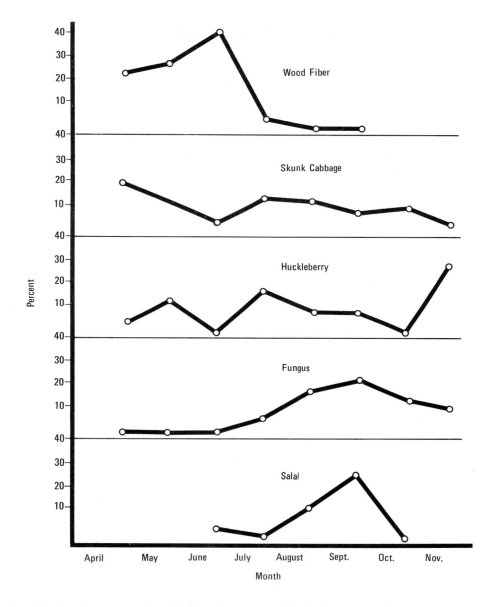

FIG. 48. - - Percent composition of five most important plants identified in analysis of 288 stomach samples of black bear, collected during 1952, 1953 and 1954 in Grays Harbor County, Washington.

## Study II—North Olympic Peninsula

The second study showed the presence of 16 major food items or categories of items. All bear were taken during control operations. Identification of major food items only was done in the field. No composition data was taken. Results are shown in Table 42.

113

TABLE 42.—Results of food analysis for major food items only of 205 black bear stomach samples on the northern part of the Olympic Peninsula in western Washington, during 1967, 1968 and 1969.

| Food Item[a] | Percent frequency |
|---|---|
| Salal | 32 |
| Salmonberry | 30 |
| Grasses | 22 |
| Insects | 20 |
| Huckleberry | 19 |
| Skunk cabbage | 17 |
| Sapwood | 10 |
| Debris & unidentified material | 9 |
| Clover | 7 |
| Birds, fish and mammals | 5 |
| Blackberry | 4 |
| Apple | 4 |
| Elderberry | 3 |
| Devil's club | 2 |
| Fungus | 2 |
| Cascara | 1 |

[a]Listed in order of frequency

## Study III—Damage and Non-Damage Study Areas

The latest study was conducted by personnel working on the Cooperative Black Bear Study. Both scat and stomach samples were collected from bear on the damage and non-damage study areas. Disparity in sample sizes precludes a statistically valid comparison of either the scat or the stomach samples on a damage to non-damage basis. Results do, however, show apparent trends in the use of various food items.

Twenty-one food items were identified from analysis of 62 stomach samples; 51 samples from the study area and 11 from the non-damage study area (Table 43). The five most important food items, based on mean percent composition, were salal, grass, devil's club, insects and skunk cabbage. The high percent composition of salmonberry and false dandelion in samples from the non-damage study area as compared to the much lower values in the damage area are significant differences noted. The number one food item in the damage study area based on percent composition is salal, while it ranks near the bottom in utilization in the non-damage study area. Use of salal on the damage area compares with its position as number one in canopy coverage (Table 21) for key food species in the vegetation survey discussed previously. Although number one in both the damage and non-damage study areas, utilization of salal in the non-damage area was quite low. Canopy coverage for false dandelion, while low in both areas, was four times as great in the damage as in the non-damage area. This contrasts, however, with the much greater percent composition of false dandelion in the diet of non-damage area bear (21 percent) as compared to the damage area bear (5 percent).

114

TABLE 43.—Percent frequency and composition of 21 food items identified in analysis of stomach contents from 62 western Washington black bear, damage (51 samples) and non-damage (11 samples) areas compared, April through October, 1964, 1965 and 1966.

| Food Item[a] | % Frequency | | | % Composition | | |
|---|---|---|---|---|---|---|
| | Damage | Non-Damage | X | Damage | Non-Damage | X |
| Salal | 31 | 9 | 27 | 18 | 2 | 15 |
| Grass | 22 | 27 | 23 | 14 | 20 | 15 |
| Devil's club | 25 | 18 | 24 | 9 | 18 | 10 |
| Insects | 33 | 18 | 31 | 11 | 3 | 9 |
| Skunk cabbage | 22 | 9 | 19 | 10 | 2 | 8 |
| False dandelion | 14 | 36 | 18 | 5 | 21 | 8 |
| Cascara | 16 | 9 | 15 | 9 | 7 | 8 |
| Wood (bark, sapwood) | 29 | .. | 24 | 8 | .. | 6 |
| Salmonberry | 8 | 36 | 13 | 3 | 22 | 6 |
| Birds, fish & mammals | 12 | .. | 10 | 6 | .. | 5 |
| Huckleberry | 18 | 9 | 16 | 4 | 0.5 | 4 |
| Fungus | 8 | .. | 6 | 3 | .. | 2 |
| Horsetail | 2 | 9 | 3 | 2 | 3 | 2 |
| Black caps | 4 | .. | 3 | 1 | .. | 0.8 |
| Trailing blackberry | 2 | .. | 2 | 0.9 | .. | 0.7 |
| Oregon grape | 2 | .. | 2 | 0.8 | .. | 0.5 |
| Clover | 2 | .. | 2 | 0.4 | .. | 0.3 |
| Himalayan blackberry | 2 | .. | 2 | 0.2 | .. | 0.1 |
| Hemlock twigs | 2 | .. | 2 | 0.1 | .. | 0.02 |
| Bitter cherry | 2 | .. | 2 | 0.1 | .. | 0.02 |
| Waterleaf | 2 | .. | 2 | 0.1 | .. | 0.02 |

[a]Listed in order of mean percent composition.

Twenty-six food items were identified from analysis of 227 scat samples; 35 samples from the damage study area and 192 from the non-damage study area (Table 44). The five most important food items, based on mean percent composition, were false dandelion, salmonberry, grass, devil's club and skunk cabbage. Neither false dandelion nor salmonberry ranked among the top five in the stomach analysis. While insects and salal ranked high in the stomach analysis, neither rated a place among the top five here. While these differences could probably be explained on the basis of the markedly different sample sizes, differential digestibility of food items and other variables involved in sample collection, no specific attempt was made to do so during the study. What is readily apparent is the differing picture of black bear food habits one could derive by reliance on a single method of analysis. Marked differences between the damage and non-damage area, such as those noted in the stomach analysis, are not present in these data. False dandelion, salmonberry and grass all received a high rate of use in both study areas. Salal received equal, low ratings of 3 percent composition in both study areas here, whereas it was ranked number one in the damage area and near the bottom in the non-damage area stomach analysis data.

Wood fiber residues ranked highest in frequency and composition for the damage study area as compared to the non-damage study area in both the scat and stomach analysis.

TABLE 44.—Percent frequency and composition of 26 food items identified in analysis of 227 scat samples of western Washington black bear, damage (35 samples) and non-damage (192 samples) areas compared, April through September, 1964, 1965 and 1966.

| Food Item[a] | % Frequency | | | % Composition | | |
|---|---|---|---|---|---|---|
| | Damage | Non-Damage | X | Damage | Non-Damage | X |
| False dandelion | 29 | 44 | 42 | 23 | 23 | 23 |
| Salmonberry | 26 | 44 | 41 | 14 | 23 | 21 |
| Grass | 29 | 36 | 35 | 21 | 21 | 21 |
| Devil's club | 6 | 17 | 15 | 3 | 7 | 6 |
| Skunk cabbage | 11 | 12 | 12 | 2 | 3 | 3 |
| Salal | 11 | 6 | 7 | 3 | 3 | 3 |
| Cascara | 5 | 5 | 5 | 3 | 3 | 3 |
| Wood (bark, sapwood) | 14 | 7 | 8 | 6 | 0.8 | 2 |
| Huckleberry | 9 | 7 | 6 | 5 | 0.9 | 2 |
| Red elderberry | . . | 6 | 5 | . . | 3 | 2 |
| Clover | . . | 6 | 5 | . . | 2 | 2 |
| *Rubus* spp. | . . | 4 | 3 | . . | 2 | 2 |
| *Ribes* spp. | . . | 4 | 3 | . . | 3 | 2 |
| Horsetail | 3 | 5 | 4 | 3 | 0.7 | 1 |
| Unknown items | 9 | 5 | 4 | 4 | 1 | 1 |
| Trailing blackberry | 6 | 2 | 2 | 6 | 0.7 | 1 |
| Insects | 11 | 9 | 10 | 2 | 0.5 | 0.7 |
| Birds, fish and mammals | . . | 3 | 2 | . . | 0.9 | 0.7 |
| Black caps | . . | 1 | 0.9 | . . | 0.8 | 0.7 |
| Apple | 3 | 0.5 | 0.9 | 3 | 0.1 | 0.5 |
| Fungus | 5 | 2 | 1 | 0.7 | 0.4 | 0.4 |
| Thimbleberry | . . | 1 | 0.9 | . . | 0.5 | 0.4 |
| Sedge | . . | 2 | 1 | . . | 0.2 | 0.2 |
| Woodrush | . . | 0.5 | 0.4 | . . | 0.3 | 0.2 |
| Moss | . . | 1 | 0.9 | . . | 0.1 | 0.1 |
| Waterleaf | . . | 0.5 | 0.4 | . . | T[b] | T |

[a]Listed in order of mean percent composition.
[b]Trace amount, less than .05 percent.

## DISCUSSION

Tree sapwood was found from April through September in 23 percent of the stomach samples collected in the 1952-54 study. At 15 percent composition it was the most important constituent in the diet. Frequency of sapwood was highest in April, May and June, with a peak of 66 percent in June. Percent frequency and composition of sapwood in this same area was lower in 1964, 1965 and 1966, 4 and 3 percent respectively. Sapwood was found only in June in the latter time period. The 1967-1969 study on the northern part of the Olympic Peninsula showed sapwood occurring in 10 percent of the samples from April through June, with a peak frequency of 32 percent in May. These values show that sapwood use varies from year to year in the same area, between areas and with respect to the period of use in different areas. Why these differences occur is unknown. Sapwood use is highest during the "negative foraging period" following the bear's emergence from the den in the

116

spring. This period was defined by Jonkel (1962) as the period when the bear lost weight after leaving the den until a pattern of weight gain was achieved in the summer, the "positive foraging period." This period of high sapwood use coincides with formation of new sapwood, which allows the bark to "slip" easily and thus make the sapwood more accessible, and a relative low abundance of other preferred food items early in the growing season.

Comparison of data between these various studies, as stated previously, should be approached with caution. With this in mind, however, one can see that the diet of western Washington black bear is primarily vegetal supplemented with small amounts of animal material (Figure 49). Without regard to

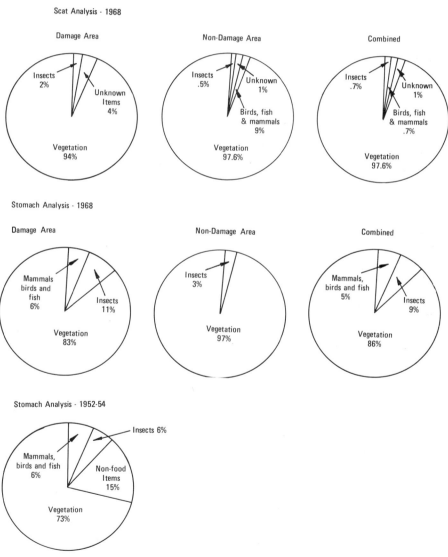

FIG. 49. - - Percent composition of major diet groups for studies shown in Tables 41, 43 and 44.

117

any specific ranking or order of preference, the ten most important plant food items appear to be false dandelion, salmonberry, grass, salal, devil's club, skunk cabbage, cascara, huckleberry, fungus and sapwood.

Ripe salal fruit was used in all areas in late summer, with a peak in August and September. The higher use of salal in damage areas can be attributed to the utilization of new leaves, blossoms and green fruit which was not evident in non-damage areas. Heavier use of salmonberry in non-damage areas is attributed to a noticeably higher use of leaves and shoots than in damage areas. A high incidence of sapwood in the diet is generally associated with a low incidence of salmonberry. Conversely, high use of salmonberry in the diet is associated with a low incidence of sapwood. No cause and effect relationship could be determined from available data. A similar pattern seems to be present between the use of false dandelion and sapwood. Peak use of sapwood and salmonberry occurred consecutively one month apart, in May and June respectively, in the north Olympic Peninsula area. A similar pattern with peak use of sapwood in June and salmonberry in July was noted in the 1964-66 Grays Harbor study. These patterns support the theory that sapwood feeding declines with an increase in more preferred food species such as salmonberry, i.e. transition from the "negative foraging period" to the "positive foraging period" coincides with the decline in sapwood feeding.

# DISEASE, PARASITES AND HEMATOLOGY

Few studies have been made to determine the ecto- and endoparasites of black bear. A study by King et al. (1960) of 306 wild bear captured in New York State, is the most extensive to date. Ectoparasites were very scarce. Lice (*Trichodectes* sp.) were found on 23 bear and ticks (*Ixodes* sp.) on only two. Roundworms (*Toxascaris* sp.) were fairly common, occurring in 20 of 65 specimens. Lungworms of the genus *Crenosoma* were found in six specimens. Microfilariae (*Dirofilaria ursi*) were present in blood smears from 47 of 101 black bear examined. Three of 49 bear examined for trichinae tested positive. In one specimen examined for blood calcium, magnesium and phosphorus, the respective values were 11.25, 7.35 and 2.35 milligrams per 100 milliliters.

Rausch (1961) found no ectoparasites on Alaska black bear. He found adults of the nematode *Dirofilaria ursi,* common in New York black bear, in only one black bear in Alaska.

Hatler (1967) found intestinal parasites in 12 of 16 bear examined in interior Alaska. Most were of the family Ascaridae. Two specimens had infestations of 53 and 249 respectively.

External parasites found by Jonkel and Cowan (1971) were ticks (*Dermacentor andersoni*), fleas (*Arctopsylla ursi*) and lice (*Trichodectes pinguis*). Ticks were the only numerous parasite. The nematode *Dirofilaria ursi* was found in two bear. The tapeworm *Taenia saginata* was occasionally collected from black bear scat. One infection of hookworm, probably *Unicinaria yuko-nensis,* was found in an adult female.

## DISEASES AND PARASITES

Studies were conducted by personnel of the College of Veterinary Medicine at Washington State University to determine the incidence of external and internal parasites on black bear. Specimens were collected in western Washington. No external parasites or instances of tissue pathology were identified.

Continuing studies of the salmon (poisoning) disease by Dr. R. Keith Farrell, D.V.M., show that the black bear has a role in transmission of this disease complex. The following information is a result of Dr. Farrell's studies on black bear and is excerpted from a report by Dr. Farrell to the Department of Game.

"Two clinical disease entities have been demonstrated in dogs after ingesting salmon and trout infected with the metacercariae of *Nanophyetus salmincola*—the salmon (poisoning) disease complex and Elokomin fluke fever. Metacercariae of this fluke are found in salmon (*Oncorhynchos* spp.), and trout (*Salmo* spp.), Pacific giant salamanders (*Dicamptodon ensatus*), river lampreys and brook lampreys (*Lampetra* spp.), reticulate sculpins (*Cottus perplexus*) and redside shiners (*Richardsonius balteatus*) of the Pacific Coast, and in migrating salmon and trout of the Pacific Ocean originating from such states. Metacercariae have been found as far north as the fifty-ninth parallel and as far south as San Francisco. The reported geographic distribution and occurrence of this fluke have increased markedly since 1927.

Salmon (poisoning) disease is the name given to the disease of dogs resulting from ingestion of raw salmon and trout that carry rickettsia-infected metacercariae of the fluke *N. salmincola.* Although two disease agents are now known to be transmitted by these flukes, the symptoms produced by the concurrent infection of these two agents are recognized as salmon (poisoning) disease of dogs.

The generic name of one of these infectious agents was designated as *Neorickettsia helminthoeca.* The second rickettsia-like agent was called the Elokomin fluke fever (EFF) agent. The EFF agent, which was originally isolated from salmon from the Elokomin River in southwestern Washington state, awaits further studies; thus, it is premature to assign a generic name to it at this time. Although easily isolated experimentally, *N. helminthoeca* has never been demonstrated singly in naturally infected dogs, but has so far been found only in combination with EFF.

The EFF agent was first isolated by the simple procedure of feeding raw salmon and trout to a black bear which sickened on the 12th day after feeding. Blood from the infected bear was then transferred to dogs and the disease characterized. The bear is refractory to the well known *N. helminthoeca* allowing the EFF agent to be separated by bear passage. Eight cases of Elokomin fluke fever have been produced in bear by fish feeding with subsequent dog passage. It is of interest to note that a 9th bear was immune to the disease. This bear was captured in the Aberdeen, Washington area and assumed to have had previous fish contact.

Susceptible bear refused feed from the 9th to 12th day after a fish meal, and exhibited diarrhea and other signs of illness. Appearance of the animals varied from a mild lethargy to lateral recumbancy from which they were aroused with difficulty. Most animals were sacrificed during the acute phase for characterization of the disease in dogs. For this reason, mortality figures are not available. However, two bear made uneventful recoveries without treatment. One bear recently fed 3, 6-inch steelhead and 4, 4-inch silver salmon showed bile blockage with necrosis of the gall bladder sufficient to have caused the death of the bear if he had not been killed for further studies and transfer. This bear showed a fluke population of 64,000 in the small intestine.

The EFF agent appears to play a part in the well known salmon disease complex of dogs as a synergistic organism in concert with *N. helminthoeca*. The incubation period in natural infection has been observed to be 9 to 12 days. The febrile response differs from that of salmon disease complex. EFF has a plateau-type febrile response instead of the sharp-peaked curve seen in salmon disease. This febrile response persists for four to seven days with a gradual return to normal in dogs that recover. Animals that do not survive show subnormal temperature before death. The febrile response is accompanied by signs of variable intensity. All animals show a marked lymphadenopathy. Most animals exhibit a mucopurulent occular discharge, anorexia, vomiting and diarrhea with dehydration. Severe depression with ataxia is observed in some animals. The lymph node involvement sometimes persists for weeks after recovery. The infectious agent can be recovered for months in clinically normal dogs.

The disease in bear is less easily diagnosed in the living animal than in dogs, but lymph nodes from dead bears have shown typical rickettsial bodies on autopsy. Adult flukes in the intestine or *N. salmincola* eggs in the stool after the initial disease signs is presumptive evidence of infection. However, it should be emphasized that recovered bears have shed fluke eggs in the feces for at least 127 days.

Examination of bear from a variety of locations in Washington in the years 1959 through 1962 revealed no flukes in the intestinal tract.

Both freezing and heating of fish inactivates the fluke and prevents rickettsial transmission. The fluke can remain viable even in severely rotted salmon."

Unidentified roundworms, of the family Ascaridae, were found in a few instances in the stomachs of black bear.

Disease appears to be uncommon in black bear in Washington and elsewhere. Although disease undoubtedly accounts for some mortality, its importance would seem low.

## HEMATOLOGY

No extensive hematological analyses were conducted during the study. Persons interested in hematology of black bear are referred to King et al. (1960), Seal et al. (1967), Svihla et al. (1955), Youatt and Erickson (1958) and Erickson and Youatt (1961).

Mineral analysis of blood from 25 black bear was performed by W. S. Zaugg of the Western Fish Nutrition Laboratory, Bureau of Sport Fisheries and Wildlife, Cook, Washington, in cooperation with project personnel. Data from these analyses follow.

Blood serum of 10 bear from the damage area and 15 bear from the non-damage area were examined for concentrations of magnesium (Mg), sodium (Na), calcium (Ca), potassium (K) and copper (Cu).

Information concerning each bear is shown in Table 45. Data showing mineral concentrations in micrograms/milliliter of serum are given in Tables 46 and 47.

TABLE 45.—Collection date and area, sex, physical condition, reproductive status of females and age of black bear specimens used for blood serum analysis.

| Sample No. | Collection date | Sex | Physical condition | Reproductive status | Age[a] | Area[b] |
|---|---|---|---|---|---|---|
| 1 | 6/19/65 | M | Fair | . . . . . . | SA | D |
| 2 | 6/23/65 | F | Good | Anestrus | Y | D |
| 3 | 5/7/65 | M | Excellent | . . . . . . | A | D |
| 4 | 5/11/65 | F | Excellent | Anestrus | A | C |
| 5A | 6/6/65 | F | Good | Anestrus | A | C |
| 5B | (duplicate) | | | | | |
| 6 | 5/26/65 | F | Excellent | Estrus | A | C |
| 7 | 5/26/65 | M | Excellent | . . . . . . | A | C |
| 8 | 5/28/65 | F | Good | Anestrus | A | D |
| 9 | 5/31/65 | F | Poor | Anestrus | Y | C |
| 10 | 5/31/65 | M | Fair | . . . . . . | SA | C |
| 11A | 5/31/65 | M | Good | . . . . . . | A | C |
| 11B | (duplicate) | | | | | |
| 12A | 6/6/65 | M | Excellent | . . . . . . | A | C |
| 12B | (duplicate) | | | | | |
| 13 | 6/9/65 | M | Good | . . . . . . | A | C |
| 14 | 6/9/65 | M | Good | . . . . . . | A | C |
| 15 | 6/10/65 | M | Poor | . . . . . . | Y | D |
| 16 | 6/12/65 | F | Good | Estrus | SA | D |
| 17 | 6/13/65 | F | Good | Estrus | A | C |
| 18 | 6/13/65 | M | Excellent | . . . . . . | A | C |
| 19 | 6/15/65 | M | Poor | . . . . . . | SA | D |
| 20 | 6/15/65 | F | Fair | Estrus | SA | D |
| 21 | 6/16/65 | F | Poor | Estrus | SA | C |
| 22 | 6/16/65 | F | Fair | Estrus | A | C |
| 23 | 6/16/65 | F | Fair | Estrus | A | C |
| 24 | 7/4/65 | M | Good | . . . . . . | Y | D |
| 25A | 5/11/65 | M | Poor | . . . . . . | A | D |
| 25B | (duplicate) | | | | | |

[a]A—adult, SA—subadult, Y—Yearling.
[b]C—non-damage area, D—damage area.

Insufficient data are present to allow valid statistical analysis. Some differences are present, however, which should be pointed out.

Concentration of magnesium is much lower in serum of bear from the

**TABLE 46.**—Mineral determinations in blood serum of black bear from non-damage area.

| Sample No. | Mineral concentrations ($\mu$g/ml serum) | | | | |
|---|---|---|---|---|---|
| | Mg | Na | Ca | K | Cu |
| 4 | 18.72 | 2910 | 112.5 | 220.0 | .250 |
| 5A | 17.94 | 3220 | 100.0 | 138.5 | No data |
| 5B | 9.10 | 2840 | 20.0 | 128.5 | .956 |
| 6 | 37.44 | 2980 | 96.0 | 183.5 | .618 |
| 7 | 19.24 | 3380 | 96.0 | 137.5 | 1.502 |
| 9 | 19.24 | 3070 | 103.5 | 200.5 | .414 |
| 10 | 19.24 | 3190 | 87.5 | 141.5 | .612 |
| 11A | 13.52 | 2680 | 45.2 | 97.5 | .544 |
| 11B | 7.02 | 2390 | 58.5 | 75.0 | .544 |
| 12A | 6.50 | 1770 | 20.0 | 213.0 | .284 |
| 12B | 13.00 | 2510 | 52.0 | 431.0 | .348 |
| 13 | 25.22 | 3720 | 118.0 | 151.0 | 1.060 |
| 14 | 9.10 | 3110 | 37.5 | 174.5 | 1.650 |
| 17 | 21.84 | 3080 | 73.5 | 132.0 | .794 |
| 18 | 8.84 | 2540 | 18.5 | 114.5 | 1.350 |
| 21 | 19.24 | 2460 | 21.5 | 493.5 | 1.850 |
| 22 | 9.36 | 3220 | 37.5 | 133.0 | .782 |
| 23 | 22.36 | 3240 | 87.5 | 165.0 | .848 |
| Mean | 16.50 | 2906 | 65.8 | 185.0 | .847 |

**TABLE 47.**—Mineral determinations in blood serum of black bear from damage area.

| Sample No. | Mineral concentrations ($\mu$g/ml serum) | | | | |
|---|---|---|---|---|---|
| | Mg | Na | Ca | K | Cu |
| 1 | 11.44 | 3050 | 108.5 | 177.5 | .564 |
| 2 | 16.64 | 3310 | 102.0 | 307.5 | .678 |
| 3 | 5.20 | 3030 | 113.5 | 150.0 | 1.200 |
| 8 | 20.28 | 3320 | 95.0 | 177.5 | 2.020 |
| 15 | 7.02 | 3080 | 12.5 | 424.5 | .534 |
| 16 | 1.56 | 1180 | 7.0 | 125.0 | .592 |
| 19 | 5.46 | 1060 | 5.1 | 192.5 | .556 |
| 20 | 7.02 | 1610 | 12.5 | 174.5 | .290 |
| 24 | 14.82 | 2930 | 95.0 | 138.0 | .242 |
| 25A | 12.48 | 3150 | 54.0 | 168.0 | .558 |
| 25B | 25.22 | 3210 | 54.5 | 170.5 | .546 |
| Mean | 11.55 | 2630 | 60.0 | 200.0 | .707 |

damage area. The range of values present, however, make any conclusions drawn somewhat less than firm. The significance of low magnesium concentrations is correlated with the importance of magnesium as a requirement for satisfactory growth, its role in calcium metabolism and other metabolic functions.

Sodium and calcium are low in several of the damage area samples as compared to non-damage samples. A deficiency in either of these minerals would result in serious consequences to the bear. Inadequate lactation, reproductive failure and interference with normal blood clotting are some of the biological results of such deficiencies.

There appears to be no over-all difference between the damage and non-damage areas with respect to potassium and copper concentrations.

Variations in concentrations between duplicate samples is probably a result of either sample contamination or differing degrees of hemolysis.

Future research should consider the importance of a complete and statistically adequate hematological study of black bear in Washington as part of any investigation comparing black bear between damage and non-damage areas.

# POPULATION CHARACTERISTICS

In this final portion of the Natural History Section, an attempt will be made to describe, within the limits of available information, certain characteristics of the black bear population in Washington. Where bias is present or suspected in reported data, this will be pointed out. Findings from other studies are used where such is lacking in this study to allow the most complete description possible of the existent population.

While the final parameters of sex ratios, age-class distribution, densities and population estimates may not withstand critical analysis, they are based on the "best available" information. Thus, while not the final answer with regard to Washington's black bear population, the description provides useful information to persons concerned with the management of the species and gives direction to persons interested in conducting further studies. Until more definitive data are available, this information stands as the only description of Washington's black bear population.

## Population Structure

While no specific attempt was made to arrive at a statistically adequate population structure, several groups of data collected during various study phases provide insight into the existing sex ratio and age-class distribution. These data are discussed below.

## Sex Ratio

Three groups of data exist from which a population sex ratio may be estimated. All have inherent biases based on reporting methods or means by which bear were collected. Of 23,020 black bear killed by sports hunters during the 5-year period, 1967 to 1971, 59 percent were identified as males and 41 percent as females for a sex ratio of 100:69. These data vary significantly from an expected even sex ratio by chi-square analysis. At least two factors operate to bias this information. Erickson (1964) found that hunters in Michigan tended to report a greater proportion of bear as males than was shown when sex was verified through examination by Department of Conservation biologists. This bias increased with greater time lapse between the kill and report date. Second, trophy hunters tend to select larger animals and this could have an effect by causing a greater selection for the larger males (Table 29 and Fig. 34).

Bear control operations accounted for 6,003 black bear of known sex during the period 1951 through 1970. Fifty-six percent were males and 44 percent females, a sex ratio of 100:79. These data were also significantly different from the expected even sex ratio by chi-square analysis. Method of capture gave differing ratios with trapping giving the highest proportion of males, 63 percent. If the assumed even sex ratio does exist in the population, this rate of capture is significantly greater than would be expected by chance indicating that trapping is selective of males. Chi-square analysis shows dog hunting to be selective of females whereas no selectivity is shown by still hunters (Table 48).

During one phase of the bear study 39 black bear, 26 males and 13 females, were captured, tagged and released. Twenty-seven resightings, either recaptures or kills, were subsequently recorded. As twice as many males existed in the known sample as females, each female recapture was considered as equal to two male captures to allow conversion of the recapture data to a probable sex ratio for the sampled population. Of the 27 relocations, 16 were males and 11 were females. Weighting the female relocations by a value of 2 gives an adjusted capture of 16 males and 22 females, or a population of 42 percent males and 58 percent females, a sex ratio of 100:138. This is not significantly different from a theoretical 100:100 sex ratio. While this sample is small, it constitutes the only known-ratio population sampled. A comparison of the data from the bear control returns and this latter study is shown in Table 48.

Hunter bias in tending to report more males killed than is actually the

TABLE 48.—Comparison of sex ratios obtained from unknown and known populations of black bear in western Washington by trapping, dog hunting and still hunting.

| Method | Bear captured—Unknown population[a] | | Bear captured—Known population[b] | |
|---|---|---|---|---|
| | Total No. | % Male | Total No. | % Male |
| Trapping | 3839 | 63[d] | 8 | 60 |
| Dog hunting | 1660 | 44[d] | 12 | 41 |
| Still hunting | 504 | 48 | 7 | 27 |
| Combined | 6003 | 56[d] | 27 | 42 |
| Sex ratio | 100:79 | | 100:138 | |

[a]All taken during control operations, 1951 through 1970.
[b]Of 39 tagged bear released, 26 were male and 13 female.
[c]Percentages adjusted to reflect 100:50 sex ratio present in marked population.
[d]Significantly different from an even sex ratio by Chi-square analysis.

124

case, and selectivity for males in the field, lessens the apparent imbalance in the sex ratio derived from sport kill data. Whether these biases and possibly other unidentified variables negate the imbalance is unknown. It is felt that the true ratio is nearer 100:100 than the raw data would indicate. While the control kill showed a lesser imbalance than sport kill with regard to an assumed even sex ratio, an imbalance still existed. This can be attributed in part to the fact that trapping, which accounted for 64 percent of the control kill, shows nearly 63 percent males captured. Taking this into account, a lesser ratio than the indicated 100:79 would be probable. In the final group, which is the only known-ratio population, a 100:138 male to female ratio was found. As this is based on a small sample size, it is not considered as significantly different from an even sex ratio.

The sex ratio of captured bear on the Big Creek Study Area in Montana (Jonkel and Cowan 1971) was 112:100 but did not differ significantly from an even sex ratio. Kills confirmed as to sex in Michigan (Erickson 1964) showed a ratio of 100:108 and was not significantly different from an even sex ratio.

In view of these considerations and as no substantive data to the contrary exists, a sex ratio of 100:100 is assumed for black bear in Washington with the understanding that a slight imbalance in favor of males probably exists. Future studies of black bear populations should include provisions for acquiring statistically adequate data on this aspect.

### Age-class Distribution

Insufficient data are available to adequately describe the age-class distribution of black bear in Washington. Some information exists, however, which provides insight into this aspect and a basis for comparison with future studies.

Sport hunters, bear control hunters and study personnel all use some

TABLE 49.—Errors in field age-estimates of 110 known-age[a] black bear.

| Known-age sample | | | Age-class determination of known-age bear based on field estimates | | | |
|---|---|---|---|---|---|---|
| Known Age-class[b] | No. | % Correctly aged by field estimate | Cubs | Yearlings | Subadults | Adults |
| Cubs | 6 | 100 | 6[c] | 0 | 0 | 0 |
| Yearlings | 15 | 67 | 3 | 10 | 0 | 0 |
| Subadults | 50 | 56 | 0 | 8 | 28 | 14 |
| Adults | 39 | 87 | 0 | 0 | 5 | 34 |
| Total | 110 | . . . | 9 | 18 | 35 | 48 |

[a]Age determined by cementum layer counts.
[b]Cubs—0-12 months; yearlings—over 12 to 24 months; subadults—over 24 to 48 months; adults—over 48 months.
[c]Underlined are number in known-age class correctly aged in the field.

method of ascribing ages to bear collected in the field. These field estimates are a combination of the individual's experience with black bear and his judgment with regard to such factors as tooth wear and growth, body size and pad size. Estimated age-classes (see footnote b, Table 49) can, if accurate, provide useful information. An opportunity to evaluate the accuracy of these field estimates was provided by 110 known-age bear for which field personnel had also ascribed age-classes. Results of this comparison are shown in Table 49. The degree of error shown for field estimates is sufficient to cast significant doubt on any age-class structure derived from field age-estimates. These data, however, provide a chance to develop correction factors which can be applied to groups of bear to which ages have been ascribed by field estimates. These factors, derived from data in Table 49, are shown in Table 50. During the period 1950 through 1970, 5,880 bear taken during control operations were assigned an age-class by field estimates. These estimates given both unadjusted (as performed in the field) and as adjusted by the correction factors in Table 50, are shown in Table 51. While the adjusted figures probably give a fair approximation of the age-class distribution of captured bear, how this compares with the actual population is unknown. Selectively by age-class, sex, capture method or other unidentified variables surely acts to some degree to inject an unknown bias into the results. The adjusted age-class structure shown in Table 51 is compared with similar data from Virginia (Stickley 1961), Michigan (Erickson and Petrides 1964) and Montana (Jonkel and Cowan 1971) in Table 52.

TABLE 50.—Correction factors to apply against field age-estimates as derived from known-age comparisons to field age-estimates.

| | |
|---|---|
| 33 % | of estimated-age cubs are actually yearlings. |
| 44 % | of estimated-age yearlings are actually subadults. |
| 5.7% | of estimated-age subadults are actually yearlings. |
| 14.2% | of estimated-age subadults are actually adults. |
| 29 % | of estimated-age adults are actually subadults. |

TABLE 51.—Unadjusted and adjusted age-class distribution of 5,880 black bear collected during the period 1950 through 1970 in western Washington.

| Age-class | % Unadjusted | % Adjusted |
|---|---|---|
| Cubs | 6.4 | 4.2 |
| Yearlings | 17.2 | 12.9 |
| Subadults | 20.5 | 40.4 |
| Adults | 55.9 | 42.5 |

Average age values from 135 known-age bear were 3.7 years for males and 6.6 years for females. Average age for the entire group was 4.7 years. Maximum age recorded for males was 14 years and for females, 27 years. This latter female may be the oldest known-age wild female black recorded to date. Age estimation by cementum layer counts becomes less precise with

126

TABLE 52.—Adjusted age structure of 5,880 black bear collected in western Washington as compared with that in Virginia, Michigan and Montana.

| Age-class | Virginia[a] % | Michigan[b] % | Montana[c] % | Washington % |
|---|---|---|---|---|
| Cub | 2 | 28 | 12 | 4.2 |
| Yearling | 29 | 18 | 17 | 12.9 |
| Total Cub & Yearling | 31 | 46 | 29 | 17.1 |
| Subadult | . . | . . | 30 | 40.4 |
| Adult | . . | . . | 41 | 42.5 |
| Total Older Bear | 69 | 54 | 71 | 82.9 |

[a]Stickley (1961): 94 bear collected in 1955 and 1956.
[b]Erickson and Petrides (1964): 158 bear collected during 1952 to 1957.
[c]Jonkel and Cowan (1971): 155 bear collected 1960 to 1965.

older bear. Errors of up to 4 years may be made with bear showing over 20 cementum annuli (Guenther 1967). Age-class composition of this group was 6 percent cubs, 12 percent yearlings, 42 percent subadults and 40 percent adults.

## Density

Gathering sufficient data to accurately describe black bear densities is difficult at best. In the heavily wooded areas of western Washington it is nearly impossible. While the following discussion is based on insufficient data to establish a truly valid density figure, perhaps the tentative values derived will provide a basis for future studies. The value of accurate density data lies in the ease with which these can then be transposed to population estimates when compared against available habitat area.

Two studies in other areas have derived density values for black bear. Erickson and Petrides (1964) determined that their 400 square mile study area in Michigan had an average of 1 bear for each 3.4 square miles based on recoveries of tagged and untagged bear. They felt this was a low estimate in view of the amount of bear sign which was present. Also, in one case of intensive trapping, they were able to capture 23 bear within a single township (36 square miles). This is approximately 1 bear per 1.6 square miles, and not all of the bear present were captured. In Montana, Jonkel and Cowan (1971), found that the density on an 80 square mile study area varied from approximately 1 bear per square mile to 1 bear per 1.7 square miles from 1959 to 1966. Their data were based on observations of a population with a substantial number tagged.

During the early 1950's, when bear damage was receiving its first serious consideration in Washington, estimates of bear densities ranged as high as 4 bear per square mile (Levin 1954). While these values may be higher than those which were actually present, they do reflect a time when densities were high. In one, two-year period in the early 1950's, over 300 black bear were taken from 8 townships (288 square miles) during control operations (op. cit.). This represents over 1 bear captured per square mile and again not all the bear present were collected. Data from the Cooperative Black Bear Study reveal an indication of density in the non-damage study area. Along one trapline, 39 different black bear were captured during the period 1964 to 1966. The line ran through parts of two townships and the shaded area (Fig. 50) represents 39 sections through which the line ran or was adjacent. While it would be inappropriate to translate this to bear density the data do indicate a rather high number of bear in the area. In the spring of 1972, during a 10 week period, 25 bear were taken from an 18 square mile damage control area on the North Fork Snoqualmie River in western Washington. As not all the bear were taken, and minimum time was available for emigration or immigration, a probable minimum density of 1.4 bear per square mile existed on the area. The area was on a commercial tree farm where forest regeneration had reached a stage where it is most susceptible to bear damage. This figure is probably the best available density figure for black bear in western Washington.

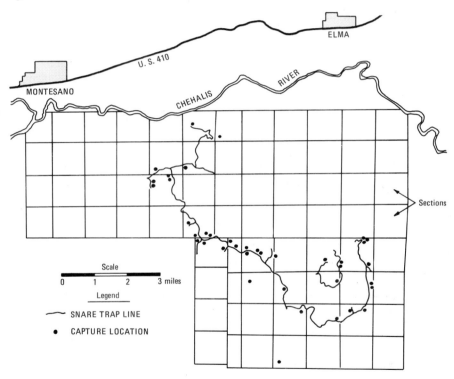

FIG. 50. - - Locations of 39 individual bear, captured during 1964, 1965 and 1966, on the non-damage study area, Grays Harbor, County, Washington.

The best estimate of average black bear density in Washington is at or slightly in excess of 1 black bear per square mile of available black bear habitat.

128

## MORTALITY

Information on natural mortality of black bear is limited and none was obtained during the Cooperative Black Bear Study. Erickson and Petrides (1964) reported 16 percent mortality in first year mortality of adult bear following tagging. Sport hunting accounted for 84 percent of the known mortality. Jonkel and Cowan (1971) reported an annual mortality of nearly 23 percent for black bear in Montana.

An interesting facet of Erickson's study was determination of the age of self-sufficiency in black bear. His data revealed that black bear cubs of either sex may be self-sufficient when as young as 5½ months and as small as 18 pounds, even though handicapped by physical injury and released on unfamiliar range (Erickson 1959).

Known mortality within a marked population of 38 black bear released on the damage and non-damage study areas during the study is shown in Table 53. The marked population, upon release, was comprised of 5 percent cubs, 18 percent yearlings, 22 percent subadults and 55 percent adults. Sport hunting accounted for 71 percent of the kill and control operations the re-

TABLE 53.—Mortality within a released sample of 38 tagged black bear, 1 to 7 years following release in western Washington.

| | Year following release | | | | | | |
|---|---|---|---|---|---|---|---|
| | Year 1 | Year 2 | Year 3 | Year 4 | Year 5 | Year 6 | Year 7 |
| Total captured to date | 12 | 13 | 19 | 19 | 20 | 20 | 21 |
| % of released population | 31 | 34 | 50 | 50 | 53 | 53 | 55 |
| Mean annual mortality indicated % | 31 | 17 | 17[a] | 13 | 11 | 9 | 8 |

[a]Over 90 percent of known mortality occurred by end year 3.

mainder. Over 90 percent of the known mortality occurred within 3 years of release, giving an average annual mortality of 17 percent. These figures reflect a maximum man-caused mortality rate in western Washington as the area was open year-round to sport hunting at the time without bag limit. Current management regulations, including classification as a game animal and specified hunting seasons and areas, should give a lower mortality rate. Natural mortality would be added to the indicated man-caused mortality rate to arrive at a total mortality rate. As Washington bear are relatively long-lived, nearly immune to any but intraspecific predation and adult populations are stable, natural mortality is probably quite low.

With the above factors in mind, the best estimate of mortality for black bear in Washington, including sport hunting, control operations and natural mortality, is determined to be between 15 and 18 percent annually. Again, future studies should include provisions for a more accurate assessment of mortality rates and their causes. In support of this mortality rate is the fact that 8.1 percent of the total population are lactating females (see Female Reproduction). This is considered to be a conservative estimate. The 8.1 percent lactating females, together with an ovulation rate of 1.9, gives an annual minimum production estimate of 15.4 percent. In a stable population annual production should equal annual mortality. In this population, which is considered to be stable, these figures are comparable.

## POPULATION ESTIMATE

There are probably as many ways to estimate a big game population as there are investigators willing to make an estimate. In this section four approaches to estimating the population of black bear in Washington will be presented. Based on evaluation of the several factors involved, a final estimate will then be established.

Harvest Method:

Currently the population is being calculated from total harvest figures. In 1972 a total of 4,316 black bear were harvested by both sport hunting and control operations. A stable population is assumed in which mortality equals production and a production rate of 20 percent is present. Thus, disregarding natural mortality, which is assumed to be negligible, for every bear harvested there exists 5 in prehunting population. A harvest of 4,316 bear then reflects a prehunting population of 21,580, which is rounded to the nearest thousand, in this case, 22,000. This figure was the estimate of black bear in Washington in 1972.

The next three approaches are based on information obtained during the Cooperative Black Bear Study. The first is quite similar to the current harvest to prehunting population ratio just discussed. It is based, however, on mortality rates derived from study data.

Mortality Rate Method:

Assume:  1) A stable population
Given:   1) Annual mortality equals 15 to 18 percent.
         2) Annual mortality equals 4,200 bear: Mean harvest, 1966 through 1971.

*then—*

(a)  $\frac{15}{100} = \frac{4200}{X}$

     X = 28,000 black bear in population based on minimum mortality

(b)  $\frac{18}{100} = \frac{4200}{X}$

     X = 23,333 black bear in population based on maximum mortality
     Population range based on estimated mortality: 23,000 to 28,000

The next estimate is based on data concerning female reproduction and total annual harvest. In the section on Female Reproduction, it was established that a minimum of 8.1 percent of the total population were lactating females and that they exhibited a mean ovulation rate of 1.9. These factors, in

130

conjunction with a known harvest rate in a stable population, allow derivation of a population estimate as follows.

Female Reproduction Data Method:

Assume:  1) A stable population
         2) No natural mortality
Given:   1) 8.1 percent of total population are lactating females
         2) An ovulation rate of 1.9 exists
         3) Mean harvest for 1966 through 1971 equals 4200 bear.

*then—*

(a) $\dfrac{4200}{1.9}$ = 2210 females with cubs in the population

(b) $\dfrac{2210}{X} = \dfrac{8.1}{100}$

     X  =  27,283 black bear in population

The last method is simply the application of estimated bear density against the amount of available habitat. For the purposes of estimating the existing population, the lower limit of the density estimate (see previous discussion on density) of 1 bear per square mile will be used. In the Big Game Status Report published annually by the Washington Department of Game, each Game Management Unit within each of the 10 departmental regions in the state is listed separately within the deer harvest section. For each of these units the amount of deer range is stated. This figure, for each unit, is the result of continuing reevaluation of deer habitat and is the best available figure in the state with regard to habitat area which is potentially capable of carrying a big game population. The area which is capable of supporting deer is greater than that which supports black bear. To arrive at an estimate of available bear habitat, arbitrary reduction factors were applied to the deer range east and west of the Cascade Mountains. Much of the deer range in eastern Washington does not support a black bear population. One region, which has no recorded harvest since 1964, was eliminated from consideration in its entirety. Total deer range in the 4 remaining regions of eastern Washington is 24,385 square miles. Much of this is in dry sagebrush or river breaks terrain which does not support black bear. Fifty percent of this area was arbitrarily determined as incapable of supporting black bear. Reducing the deer range by 50 percent gave a black bear range of 12,183 square miles in eastern Washington. WesternWashington, which is much wetter and more heavily forested, has 20,005 square miles of deer range. Black bear are more widely distributed in western Washington than in eastern Washington and occupy a greater portion of the deer range. Reducing the deer range in western Washington by 10 percent leaves about 18,005 square miles of black bear habitat. For all of Washington then, there are approximately 30,198 square miles of black bear habitat. At an average density of 1 bear per square mile, a population of 30,198 would be postulated. These calculations are summarized below.

Density Method:

Assume:    1) In 4 regions of eastern Washington with black bear populations, 50 percent of the deer range does not support black bear.

              2) In western Washington 10 percent of the deer range is not inhabited by black bear.

Given:     1) Deer range in the 4 regions of eastern Washington supporting black bear populations equals 24,385 square miles.

              2) Deer range in western Washington equals 20,005 square miles.

              3) Average black bear density equals 1 per square mile.

*then—*

(a) .50 x 24,385 = 12,192 square miles

     24,385

—12,192

     12,183 square miles of bear habitat in eastern Washington

(b) .10 x 20,005 = 2,000 square miles

     20,005

— 2,000

     18,005 square miles of bear habitat in western Washington

(c) 12,183 plus 18,005 = 30,198 square miles of black bear habitat in Washington

(d) Black bear density of 1 per square mile gives a population estimate of 30,198.

Four population estimates have been discussed. Addition of natural mortality, if known, to the Harvest Method first discussed, or the Female Reproduction Method, would increase these estimates. Natural mortality is included in the Mortality Method and does not enter into the Density Method discussed last. It is felt that the estimate derived from the data on female reproduction best approaches the actual population although no measure of the statistical validity of any of the methods has been made. With these factors in mind, the best estimate of the black bear population in Washington is determined to be in the range of 27,000 to 30,000.

## SUMMARY

### Bear Movements

1. Black bear movements were studied through the use of ear-tagged bear and monitoring of radio-collared bear.

2. Thirty-eight black bear were captured, tagged and released, 14 from the damage and 24 from the non-damage study area.

3. Mean relocation distances for male and female black bear in the damage study area were 5.3 and 1.4 miles, respectively; for the non-damage study area, 1.73 and 1.56 miles, respectively.

4. The longest relocation distance was for an adult male in the damage area killed 14.5 miles from the release site.

5. No incidence of movement between the damage and non-damage study areas was noted.

6. Relocation data from ear-tagged black bear suggest that they remain in the same general area from year to year and that emigration is not common.

7. Nine of 16 bear originally radio-collared were successfully monitored for periods of 1.8 to 7.1 months.

8. Areas occupied average 19.9 and 2.04 square miles for males and females, respectively.

9. No overlap in occupied areas of adult males was noted.

10. Areas occupied by females overlapped with those of males and occasionally with other females. No conflict between bear occupying overlapping areas was noted.

11. Relocation data on radio-collared bear suggests a diurnal behavior pattern for western Washington black bear.

12. Although data obtained were from a single radio-collared bear, it was established that some western Washington black bear do have a dormant period of nearly three months, even in relatively mild winters.


## Reproduction

1. Peak of breeding season extends generally from mid-June to mid-July. Spermatozoic activity in the male preceeds and exceeds the period of receptivity in the female. Peak of estrus was reached in late June and maintained into July for bear in western Washington.

2. The female black bear has a seasonally constant estrus, that is, she remains in heat until bred, or failing contact with a male, until ovarian degeneration.

3. Ovulation is induced through breeding.

4. Females which are lactating do not develop mature follicles, exhibit estrus nor accept males during the breeding season. This lactation anestrus explains in part the alternate year pregnancies typical of black bear.

5. Gestation is approximately 220 days. Delayed implantation (usually in early December) of the embryo is characteristic. Post-implantation development occurs during the 6 to 8 week period prior to parturition in late January or early February.

6. Implantation sites in the reproductive tract are noted by the presence of placental scars and are useful as indicators of reproduction. A mean scar rate of 1.88 was noted.

7. The presence of corpora lutea is used as an indicator of ovulation rates. A mean ovulation rate of 1.9 was noted.

8. An average lactation rate of 16 percent and estrus rate of 26 percent was found for 378 female black bear collected over a 3-year period.

9. Youngest age of successful reproduction noted for Washington bear was 3.4 years. Earliest corpora lutea formation noted was June 16. Sexual maturity was evident in 44 percent of the females in their fourth summer. All females 5½ years old or older were sexually mature.

10. Data suggest that successful reproduction may be possible to age 19

in the wild. A female, subsequently determined by cementum layer counts to be 26 years old, was observed to be in estrus in 1965.

11. Lactating females comprise 8.1 percent of the total population.

## Physical Characteristics

1. Mean weight for known-age male and female black bear 5 years old and over in western Washington was 221 pounds and 142 pounds respectively.

2. Track sizes (right hind pad length plus width) less than 6 inches indicate cubs and those greater than 10 inches, adult males.

3. Mean zygomatic widths for known-age male and female black bear in western Washington over 5 years old are 175 and 152 millimeters, respectively.

4. Size of bacula were highly correlated with age, however, the difference between age groups was not sufficient to allow accurate age determinations.

5. Canine root canal openings are closed in all females over 3 years and in males over 4 years of age.

6. Canine eruption can be used to estimate the age of black bear. Yearlings show no dentine above the alveolar fossae; if any dentine shows, the bear are at least 3 years old; if the dentino-enamel junction is entirely above the gum line, the bear is usually at least 5 years old; if the dentino-enamel junction is 5mm or more above the gum line, the bear is at least 10 years old.

7. Incidence of black bear in poor physical condition increases from 25 percent in April to a peak of 36 percent in June. General condition improves from this point.

8. Percentage of bear with good coats ranged from 72 percent following emergence in the spring, to a low of 12 percent in July, and back to 71 percent in late fall.

## Food Habits

1. Tree sapwood was found from April through September in 23 percent of 288 stomach samples collected in a food habit study in 1952-1954.

2. The diet of western Washington black bear is primarily vegetation supplemented with small amounts of animal material. The ten most important plant food items, without regard to order of preference, are false dandelion, salmonberry, grass, salal, devil's club, skunk cabbage, cascara, huckleberry, fungus and sapwood.

3. Sapwood use is highest following the bear's emergence from the den in the spring. This period of high sapwood use coincides with formation of new sapwood, which allows the bark to "slip" easily and thus make the sapwood more accessible, and a relative low abundance of other preferred food items early in the growing season.

## Disease, Parasites and Hematology

1. Black bear were shown to have a role in transmission of the salmon (poisoning) disease complex.

134

2. Disease is uncommon in black bear in Washington.

3. No external parasites or instances of tissue pathology were noted in Washington black bear.

4. Magnesium concentrations in blood were lower in bear from the damage as compared to bear from the non-damage study area.

5. Sodium and calcium levels in the blood were low in some damage area bear compared to non-damage area bear.

6. No over-all differences between damage and non-damage areas were noted for potassium and copper concentrations in the blood.

## Population Characteristics

1. An average of 59 percent of the sport harvest from 1967 to 1971 were males. Of 6,003 bear of known sex taken by control operations during the period 1951 through 1970, 56 percent were male. Sixty-three percent of the bear caught by trapping were male. Dog hunting was selective of females.

2. A sex ratio of 100:100 with a slight imbalance to males is the best estimate for Washington black bear populations.

3. Average ages of 3.7 years for males and 6.6 years for females was found in a sample of 135 known-age bear. Maximum age for males was 14 years and for females 27 years.

4. Adjusted age-class distribution of 5,880 bear taken during control operations was found to be 4.2 percent cubs, 12.9 percent yearlings, 40.4 percent subadults and 42.5 percent adults.

5. The best estimate of average black bear density in Washington is at or slightly in excess of 1 black bear per square mile of available black bear habitat.

6. Black bear cubs may be self-sufficient when as young as 5½ months.

7. Mortality for black bear in Washington is between 15 and 18 percent annually.

8. The black bear population in Washington is estimated to be between 27,000 and 30,000.

# SECTION III

# MANAGEMENT

In this final section, statewide harvest and management are discussed. Included is information on control operations, a summary of historical management regulations and a presentation of current management objectives as they relate to existing seasons and bag limits.

# BLACK BEAR HARVEST

Black bear harvest in Washington is comprised of both sport and control harvest. Control harvest has averaged 4.5 percent of total harvest since records began in 1951.

TABLE 54.—Population estimates, annual sport harvest and control harvest of black bear in Washington, 1950 through 1972.

| Year | Population estimate | Annual sport harvest | Control harvest | Year | Population estimate | Annual sport harvest | Control harvest |
|------|---------|---------|---------|------|---------|---------|---------|
| 1950 | 40,000 | 5,200 | . . . | 1962 | 25,000 | 8,700 | 685 |
| 1951 | 40,000 | 7,600 | 5 | 1963 | 25,000 | 6,900 | 658 |
| 1952 | 40,000 | 8,000 | 108 | 1964 | 25,000 | 8,100 | 541 |
| 1953 | 32,000 | 6,700 | 187 | 1965 | 25,000 | 7,400 | 611 |
| 1954 | 40,000 | 9,100 | 165 | 1966 | 20,000 | 4,710 | 460 |
| 1955 | 35,000 | 6,600 | 154 | 1967 | 20,000 | 3,180 | 450 |
| 1956 | 32,000 | 6,700 | 115 | 1968 | 22,000 | 4,150 | 426 |
| 1957 | 28,000 | 5,200 | 87 | 1969 | 22,000 | 3,410 | 419 |
| 1958 | 30,000 | 6,900 | 137 | 1970 | 22,000 | 3,470 | 226 |
| 1959 | 30,000 | 6,200 | 203 | 1971 | 22,000 | 4,100 | 216 |
| 1960 | 30,000 | 8,900 | 167 | 1972 | 27,000 | 3,400 | 227 |
| 1961 | 25,000 | 5,500 | 412 | Total | . . . . . | 140,120 | 6,659 |

## SPORT HUNTING

Sport harvest of black bear has varied substantially over the years. A high of 9,100 bear was reached in 1954 (Table 54). Near record harvests of 8,900 and 8,700 were taken in 1960 and 1962 (Table 54). Western Washington has provided the bulk of harvest through the years with an average of 76 percent of total sport harvest since 1960. Eastern Washington, with somewhat less black bear habitat, shorter seasons and more restrictive bag limits, has provided an average of 24 percent of the total harvest (Tables 1 and 55). The lowest sport harvest was 3,180 in 1967 (Table 54).

Harvest data prior to and following 1965, show two quite different patterns. During the 6-year period from 1960 through 1965, the average statewide harvest was 7,583; 1,628 on the eastside and 5,955 on the westside (Table 55). During the following 7 years the average harvest dropped to 3,760 statewide; 1,104 on the eastside and 2,656 on the westside (Table 55). This drop is shown graphically in Fig. 51. Decreased harvest was primarily on the westside. Many persons thought the decline was a result of a precipitous population crash. This, undoubtedly, was not the case. A combination of factors existed which may be correlated with the decrease. First, black bear have a

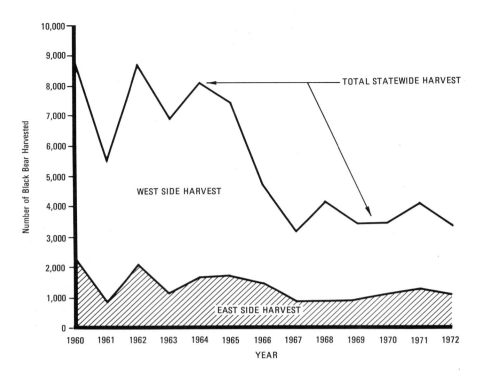

FIG. 51. - - Sport black bear harvest, eastern and western Washington compared, 1960 through 1972.

low reproductive rate. In western Washington, where most of the harvest decrease occurred, extensive areas of actual or potential black bear habitat have been undergoing change for many years. Much of this change is correlated with forest management practices, the remainder with highway construction, housing and recreational development, and other miscellaneous land use practices. It is typical of big game populations which have been maintained naturally or even artificially, at or above the carrying capacity of an area to suffer reductions when the carrying capacity of the land is reduced. These reductions may be rapid, affecting all segments of the population as in massive die-offs of deer following severe winters or overutilization of available range, or less profound in species such as bear through such regulatory mechanisms as lowered cub survival and reduced natality. When these populations rebound from subsequent lows, they normally stabilize at a level above the low point but also significantly below the previous high. This new level reflects the current carrying capacity of the range. Data are insufficient to support this thesis here. Field personnel, however, do feel that reproductive rates declined to below normal levels prior to the harvest decline. This decline in reproduction was, in part, a response to less than optimum habitat conditions throughout much of the black bear range as reforested areas reached maturity. Early seral stands, with larger quantities of forage, had contributed to a population level that the more mature stands, with decreased forage, could not support. This decline in reproduction was evidenced, in part, by the notable decline in sport harvest. Bear which should have provided the harvest at the time, had simply not been born, or once born, had not survived.

138

**TABLE 55.—Mean sport black bear harvest for Washington, 1960-1965 and 1966-1972.**

| Period | Mean sport harvest | | |
| --- | --- | --- | --- |
| | Eastside | Westside | Statewide |
| 1960-1965 . . . . . . . . . . . . . . . . . . . . . . . . . . . . | 1,628 | 5,955 | 7,583 |
| 1966-1972 . . . . . . . . . . . . . . . . . . . . . . . . . . . . | 1,104 | 2,656 | 3,760 |
| % statewide harvest 1960-1972. . . . . . | 24 | 76 | . . . . |
| % decrease in harvest since 1960 . . . . . | 33 | 55 | 50 |

An additional factor which had a definite impact on harvest was the implementation of a black bear tag requirement in 1967. This tag requirement apparently had the result of reducing the number of black bear hunters. Following a year of reduced harvest in 1966, the tag served to lower the pressure on the bear population. Total bear hunters declined from 35,560 and 32,700 in 1965 and 1966, respectively, to 22,500 in 1967. Thus, the harvest decline is a result of a combination of factors, the most important of which, while not directly supported by available data, is probably a realignment of the population with respect to the carrying capacity of the land through a temporary reduction in reproductive rates and increased juvenile mortality. In support of this conclusion is the fact that harvest rates have been relatively stable since 1968. The 1972 harvest equaled approximately 12 to 13 percent of the current population estimate of 27,000 to 30,000 bear. Since the low point in 1967, harvest has not exceeded 15.3 percent of this estimate. A minimum annual production of 15.4 percent was established previously and thus, it would appear that current harvest figures are within safe limits.

Based on the data from bear report cards during the period 1967 to 1972, the harvest was comprised of 6.3 percent cubs, 35.7 percent yearlings and 58.0 percent adults. Because of wide variations in aging techniques and capabilities of hunters to accurately assign bear to age-classes, these data are not comparable to those described earlier under Age-class Distribution. Percent of males in the harvest ranged from 56 to 62 percent during this same period.

An average 74.5 percent of the total sport harvest occurs during September and October (Table 56). Even in western Washington, which has a limited bear season during the period from April through August in addition to the fall season, some 61 to 67 percent of the total harvest is taken during

**TABLE 56.—Mean percent of sport black bear harvest by month, 1967 through 1972.**

| Year | Mean percent of sport harvest | | | | | | | |
| --- | --- | --- | --- | --- | --- | --- | --- | --- |
| | April | May | June | July | Aug. | Sept. | Oct. | Nov. |
| 1967 | 0 | 0 | 4 | 3 | 6 | 57 | 26 | 4 |
| 1968 | 2 | 3 | 6 | 8 | 10 | 38 | 30 | 3 |
| 1969 | 1 | 3 | 2 | 5 | 8 | 37 | 38 | 6 |
| 1970 | 2 | 6 | 6 | 7 | 4 | 34 | 36 | 5 |
| 1971 | 3 | 6 | 6 | 7 | 4 | 39 | 34 | 1 |
| 1972 | 2 | 4 | 5 | 6 | 5 | 41 | 37 | 0 |
| Mean | 1.7 | 3.7 | 4.8 | 6.0 | 6.2 | 41 | 33.5 | 3.2 |

139

September and October (Big Game Status Report, Washington Department of Game, 1967 through 1972). Without extended seasons on the westside, some 30 percent of the current harvest might not be taken. This might only compound the present situation with respect to bear damage.

## CONTROL OPERATIONS

Control operations have been carried out in areas of bear damage since the early 1950's. Data from the Cooperative Black Bear Study indicated that concentration of control efforts in specific damage areas rather than widespread control over large areas is more economical in respect to manpower requirements and operating costs. Most importantly, however, this concentration of effort reduces the number of bear taken while at the same time proving more effective in reducing bear damage. A history of control efforts and methods was presented earlier in the Forest Relationship Section.

Control operations have taken approximately 4.5 percent of the total harvest in Washington since 1951. In 1972 the take amounted to 3.6 percent of the total harvest. Control harvest for each year since 1951 is given in Table 54.

## MANAGEMENT REGULATIONS

Historical management regulations are shown in Table 1 and have been discussed in the Introduction to this bulletin. In summary, a season of 15 days or less was established for most counties of the state, with a one-bear limit east of the Cascades and a two-bear limit in western Washington, when the Department of Game was first organized in 1933. Various bag limits were imposed until in 1946 the limit was lifted in western Washington. A limit of 3 bear was imposed for King, Snohomish, Whatcom and Skagit counties in 1970, and reduced to 2 in 1971. The black bear was declared a predator in Clallam, Grays Harbor, Jefferson, Kitsap and Mason counties in 1951. This classification was maintained until 1969 when the bear was again classified as a game animal statewide.

As of this writing, in the spring of 1973, the black bear is classified as a game animal statewide. A bag limit of 2 bear exists in King, Snohomish, Skagit and Whatcom counties. There is no bag limit in the remainder of western Washington. A bag limit of 1 bear exists in eastern Washington. The season opening in eastern Washington is usually set in coordination with the opening of the grouse season in early September and the close of the general deer season in late October or early November. Seasons are more variable in western Washington. Generally an April opening is set for the counties of the Olympic Peninsula, southwest Washington and southern Puget Sound outside all the national forests except for Olympic National Forest, which is included. In July the remainder of western Washington outside of the national forests is opened and then in early September the remaining areas within the national forests are opened.

As discussed earlier, data obtained during the Cooperative Black Bear Study showed that a specific black bear could normally be expected to inhabit the same general area from one year to the next during a particular season. In addition, this occupied area was smaller than expected, averaging approximately 20 square miles for males and 2 square miles for females. During the bear study, interest in using sportsmen to alleviate bear damage was often expressed. With this objective in mind and information on areas occupied by black bear, a plan evolved through which it was hoped that both an increase in recreational opportunity for sportsmen and reduced bear damage might be obtained.

This plan resulted in a major revision of black bear hunting seasons at the January 1973 Game Commission meeting. The plan, developed by the Department of Game in coordination with other state agencies, sportsmen's groups throughout the state, and private industry, involved the establishing of 16 spring damage units open to black bear hunting from April 1 to June 30. Selection of the units, ranging in size from 7 to 500 square miles, was based on the existence of bear damage, accessibility to sport hunters and suitability for sport hunting efforts. The area outside of the 16 spring damage units was closed to bear hunting, thus concentrating spring bear hunting in current bear damage areas.

The only reason for a spring bear season in the past has been to alleviate bear damage. As these seasons were generally open throughout much of western Washington, a concentration of effort necessary to satisfactorily reduce damage was not achieved. By further concentrating sport hunting in areas with current damage, sportsmen will be able to more effectively reduce this damage.

A redesigned black bear report card is in use to provide information on the success of the program. A more detailed discussion of the black bear tag and its associated Black Bear Report Card is given later. Additionally, aerial and ground surveys of damage areas within the spring bear units will be conducted to determine whether damage is being reduced.

The goal of this new program is to put sportsmen in the role of assisting in alleviation of a game damage problem while increasing their own recreational opportunities. As sportsmen's success increases, the necessity for professional control of bear damage will decrease. Control snaring will not be conducted within the spring damage units during the open season.

As a large proportion of black bear taken in western Washington are taken with hounds, boundaries of spring damage units were established to facilitate hound hunting. A 3-year trial of this program is necessary to satisfactorily evaluate its potential. Changes will be incorporated each year as needed. Units may be dropped or added, and boundaries adjusted where necessary.

As mentioned earlier, a bear tag has been required to hunt black bear since 1967. The initial effect of the bear tag was to reduce hunter pressure on black bear. The opportunistic hunter who would take a bear if the occasion arose, was removed from the harvest by the tag requirement. Tag sales, with the exception of 1972, have increased each year (Table 57). Sport harvest, which is derived from the annual Game Harvest Questionnaire, has remained stable. Percent of bear report cards returned has increased each year except 1971 (Table 57). Since 1969 when the black bear was again classified as a game animal on the Olympic Peninsula, all bear hunters statewide have been required to have a tag in their possession while hunting bear.

TABLE 57.—Bear tag sales and bear report card returns compared to sport harvest, 1967 through 1972.

| Year | Number of tags sold | Number of report cards returned | % of take reported by cards | Sport harvest |
|------|------|------|------|------|
| 1967 | 12,745 | 352 | 11.1 | 3,180 |
| 1968 | 17,938 | 556 | 13.4 | 4,150 |
| 1969 | 19,759 | 596 | 17.5 | 3,410 |
| 1970 | 21,417 | 688 | 19.8 | 3,470 |
| 1971 | 22,040 | 756 | 18.4 | 4,100 |
| 1972 | 21,084 | 708 | 20.8 | 3,400 |

Attached to the tag is a report card. When first developed, this report card provided information on where the bear was taken, its sex and age. With the initiation of the spring damage units, this report card was redesigned to provide additional information which will help evaluate the program. The new card will provide information, in addition to that previously mentioned, on whether or not the bear was taken over hounds, the spring bear unit in which taken, and the name and address of the hunter. This latter information will allow follow up inquiries to acquire any additional details desired. At the end of 3-year period, the program will be evaluated to determine the success of bear damage control through the use of sports hunting.

## STUDY CONCLUSIONS

Recapitulation of the study findings is best done by keeping both the research and management aspects in mind. The Cooperative Black Bear Study was begun as a result of increased recognition of black bear damage to coniferous forest reproduction. As damage levels reached sufficient magnitude to be considered as significant factors with regard to black bear management, acquisition of information regarding bear damage became essential.

Initial research efforts were directed to determining the distribution, extent and characteristics of black bear damage. Results of questionnaires and field studies showed that bear damage was distributed throughout much of western Washington. In many areas damage was severe enough to have serious economic impact in the affected area although no method of ascribing a specific dollar value to the damage was available. Control operations were expensive to forest industry, distasteful and wasteful of a game resource. Thus, early efforts were directed to determining why black bear damage trees and what modifications of timber or bear management might help to reduce the conflicts. As these problems were considered, a lack of information relative to black bear reproduction, food habits, movements and population characteristics was encountered. It was apparent that a comprehensive research program designed to investigate these and other aspects of black bear biology was needed.

Black bear management was being accomplished primarily through establishment of seasons and bag limits. In areas where excessive damage was prevalent a year-round open season without bag limit was allowed. Lack of information concerning the biology of black bear and uncertainty with how to deal with the damage problem impaired management efforts. The primary objective of the Cooperative Black Bear Study was thus established: To develop techniques for management of black bear in Washington.

While much data obtained during the study confirmed previous contentions a considerable body of new information was developed. The fact that black bear could be expected to occupy the same areas from year to year during a given season was to prove invaluable. The size of these areas, approximately 20 square miles for males and 2 square miles for females, was equally important. Damage was often observed in 20 to 40-year-old trees. The more vigorous trees in lightly stocked stands were most frequently damaged. Sapwood use was found to be highest in the spring following the bear's emergence. This use correlated with a relatively low abundance of other preferred food items early in the growing season. Analysis of tree sapwood from damage and non-damage areas revealed no differences to which bear damage could be attributed. Information on the age of trees receiving damage, bear densities in damage areas and amounts of available forage support the thesis that bear damage results, at least in large measure, from existence of a high bear density in an area of maturing timber stands with declining carrying capacity. Lack of abundant forage in the spring is particularly important in view of the fact that bear, whether in a damage or non-damage area, continue to lose weight for 2 to 3 months following emergence. Thus, food stress is a problem in the spring for all bear, particularly for those living in maturing forests where forage abundance is declining.

The final question of "Why do bear eat sapwood?" has not been completely answered. Similar forest areas, with apparently comparable vegetation and bear densities, often reflect quite differing damage patterns. The variables which might account for these differences have not been adequately identified. Theories that bear in one area might have "learned" the habit from other bear or that the sapwood is like candy to them have not been supported by findings. What is known is that damage most often occurs in areas which are changing from what might be considered prime bear habitat to something of lesser quality. Trees most often damaged are those which are susceptible because of age, location and growth rate; the younger trees with thinner bark, located in more open stands thus allowing more vigorous growth being the best candidates for bear damage.

Based on these findings control operations were reduced from widespread area coverage to concentrated control on specific damage areas. Greater reduction of damage was achieved, and fewer acres were under professional damage control.

Bear damage is not a passing phase in forestland management. With increasing dependence on tree farming operations to sustain the timber industry, land will continually be entering the stage where it has a greater potential for bear damage. The problem facing the timber and game manager is how best to meet this situation.

Inherent in the Department of Game's responsibilities is the policy of maximizing recreational opportunities for sportsmen. Spring bear seasons have existed in western Washington solely in response to the damage problem. Sport hunting efforts have been unsuccessful in the past for the same reasons as professional control in reducing damage to acceptable levels. The effort has been spread over too large an area. Bear damage units established for the spring season in 1973 are a direct result of information gathered during the Cooperative Black Bear Study. Under new regulations, sport hunting is concentrated on 16 areas which have current bear damage. Evaluation of the program will be done over a 3-year period.

The Cooperative Black Bear Study has provided participating agencies and the forest industry opportunity for a long, in-depth look at the subject of black bear management. Not all the questions raised have been answered. Some which have been answered, at least to the satisfaction of most participants, may require additional investigations at a later date. Those which have not been answered or even addressed during the study must await future investigations.

What is important is that a management problem has been recognized and research performed to identify possible management alternatives. The success of black bear management in Washington in the future will be based almost in its entirety on the contributions of those who were involved in the many phases of the Cooperative Black Bear Study.


## SUMMARY

1. Black bear harvest is comprised of both sport and control harvest. Control harvest has averaged 4.5 percent of the total harvest since 1951.
2. The highest black bear harvest of 9,100 was recorded in 1954; the lowest, 3,180, was in 1967. Mean statewide sport harvest since 1966 is 3,760.
3. Western Washington has provided an average of 76 percent of the statewide sport harvest since 1960.
4. The drop in black bear harvest between 1964 and 1967 is attributed to a combination of factors, the most important of which was most likely a realignment of the population with respect to the carrying capacity of the land through a temporary reduction in reproductive rates and increased juvenile mortality. Implementation of a bear tag requirement also contributed to the decline.
5. Harvest rates since the low point in 1967 have ranged from 12 to 15.3 percent of the current population estimate of 27,000 to 30,000. A minimum annual production of 15.4 percent established previously indicates that current harvest rates are within safe limits.

144

6. Data from bear report cards indicate the composition of the harvest is 6.3 percent cubs, 35.7 percent yearlings and 58.0 percent adults. Percent of males in the harvest ranged from 56 to 62 percent.

7. An average of 74.5 percent of the total sport harvest occurs during September and October. In western Washington, where extended seasons are present, some 61 to 67 percent of the total harvest is taken during this same period.

8. In 1972, control operations took 3.6 percent of the total harvest.

9. Initial seasons of 15 days or less were established for most counties of the state when the Game Department was organized in 1933. The bag limit was 1 bear on the eastside and 2 bear on the westside.

10. The black bear was declared a predator in Clallam, Grays Harbor, Jefferson, Kitsap and Mason counties in 1951. This classification was maintained until 1969 when the bear was again classified as a game animal statewide.

11. Sixteen spring damage units, ranging in size from 7 to 500 square miles, were established in 1973 with the primary goal of putting the sportsmen in the role of assisting in the alleviation of a game damage problem, while at the same time increasing their own recreational opportunities.

12. A bear tag was first required in 1967 for those areas where the bear was a game animal. In 1969, with reclassification as a game animal in the Olympic and Kitsap Peninsula areas, the tag was required statewide.

13. A bear report card, attached to the tag, was redesigned to aid in evaluating the spring damage unit program.

# LITERATURE CITED

Anderson, Carl F. 1966. The significance of bear damage in forest management. U.S. For. Ser. paper, annual meeting, PNW Section of Wldl. Soc. 4 pp.

Baker, A. B. 1912. Further notes on the breeding of the American black bear in captivity. Smithsonian Misc. Coll. 59(10):1-4.

Big game status reports, 1967 through 1972. *In* files of Washington Department of Game, Olympia, Washington.

Black, Hugh C. 1958. Black bear research in New York. Trans. N. A. Wildl. Conf. 23:443-461.

Bloomfield, H. 1964. Beware of smokey the bear. The Saturday Evening Post, 237(31):68-69.

Boyce, J. S. 1961. Forest pathology. McGraw-Hill Book Co., Inc. New York, Toronto, London. 572 pp.

Bray, Olin E., and Victor G. Barnes. 1967. A literature review on black bear populations and activities. Colorado Coop. Wildl. Res. Unit, Colorado State Univ., Fort Collins. 34 pp.

Brent, Homer I., and Ellis L. Bowhay. 1956. Black bear food habits. Quart. Prog. Rpt., Proj. W-37-R-7, Washington Game Department. 7 pp.

Brown, E. R. 1950. Bear damage survey. *In* files of Washington Department of Game, Olympia, Washington.

Childs, Thomas W., and Norman P. Worthington. 1955. Bear damage to young douglas-fir. Res. Note 113, Pacific Northwest Forest and Range Expt. Sta., U.S. Forest Service, Portland, Oregon. 4 pp.

Cockrum, E. Lendell. 1962. Introduction to mammalogy. The Ronald Press Co., New York. 455 pp.

Cowan, Ian McTaggart. 1938. Geographic distribution of color phases of the red fox and black bear in the Pacific Northwest. J. Mammal. 19(2):202-206.

Crews, Arthur K. 1954. Bear control project report. Unpub. rpt. *in* files of Washington Department of Game, Olympia, Washington.

Crouch, Glen L. 1969. Animal damage to conifers on national forests in the Pacific Northwest region. U.S.D.A. Forest Service Res. Bull. PNW-28, illus. PNW For. and Range Expt. Sta., Portland, Oregon.

Eadie, W. R., and W. J. Hamilton, Jr. 1958. Reproduction in the fisher in New York. N.Y. Fish & Game J., 5:77-83.

Erickson, Albert W. 1959. The age of self-sufficiency in the black bear. J. Wildl. Mgmt. 23(4):401-405.

——————————. 1965. The black bear in Alaska. Alaska Dept. of Fish and Game. Fed. Aid in Wildl. Restr. Proj. Rpt. (Proj. W-6-R-5, Work Plan F).

——————————, John E. Nellor and George Petrides. 1964. The black bear in Michigan. Res. Bull. 4, Michigan State Univ. Agr. Exp. Sta., E. Lansing, Michigan. 102 pp.

146

———————————— and William G. Youatt. 1961. Seasonal variations in the hematology and physiology of black bears. J. Mammal. 42(2):198-203.

Farrell, R. Keith. 1968. Elokomin fluke fever: a rickettsial disease of bears and canidae. (Typewritten report) *In* files of Washington Department of Game, Olympia, Washington.

Foster, R. E. 1958. Proposed standards of measurement and procedure relating to investigations of decay. Can. Dept. of Agric. Forest Biol. Lab., Victoria, B.C. 16 pp (mimeo).

————————————, H. M. Craig, and G. W. Wallis. 1954. Studies in forest pathology. XII. Decay of western hemlock in upper Columbia Region British Columbia. Can. J. Bot. Vol. 32:145-171.

————————————, and A. T. Foster. 1951. Studies in forest pathology. VIII. Decay of western hemlock on the Queen Charlotte Islands, British Columbia. Can. J. Bot. Vol. 29:479-521.

———————————— and ————————————. 1953. Estimating decay in western hemlock (II). Suggested aids to the inventory in the Queen Charlotte Islands. British Columbia Lumberman. April:40-41.

Fritz, Emanuel. 1951. Bear and squirrel damage to young redwood. J. For. 49:651-652.

Fruton, Joseph S., and Sophia Simmonds. 1958. General biochemistry. John Wiley and Sons, Inc., New York. 1077 pp.

Gilbert, Douglas L. 1952. Bear studies. Colorado Game and Fish Dept., Fed. Aid Quart. Jan: 26-31.

Glover, Fred A. 1955. Black bear damage to redwood reproduction. J. Wildl. Mgt. 19(4):437-443.

Guenther, Keith. 1967. Population study; Black bear study. Job completion report., Fed. Aid in Wildl. Restoration, Proj. W-71-R-4, Job. No. 2. 69 pp.

————————————. 1967. Anatomical variations of western Washington black bear related to age. M.S. thesis. Univ. of Idaho, Moscow. 73 pp.

Hall, E. Raymond, and Keith R. Kelson. 1959. The mammals of North America. Vol. II. The Ronald Press Co., New York. 1083 pp.

Hatler, David Francis. 1967. Some aspects in the ecology of the black bear (*Ursus americanus*) in interior Alaska. MS Thesis (unpubl), Univ. of Alaska, College. 111 pp.

Hunt, John, and Kenneth W. Krueger. 1962. Decay associated with thinning wounds in young-growth western hemlock and douglas-fir. J. For. 60(5):336-340.

Jonkel, Charles. 1962. Black bear population studies. P-R completion report, W-98-R-1. State of Montana.

Jonkel, C.J. 1964. Estimating whole weights of black bears from hog-dressed weights. J. Wildl. Mgmt. 28(3):581.

————————————, and Ian McT. Cowan. 1971. The black bear in the spruce-fir forest. Wildl. Mono. No. 27, Wildl. Soc. 57 pp.

King, John M., Hugh C. Black and Oliver H. Hewitt. 1960. Pathology, parasitology and hematology of the black bear in New York. N.Y. Fish & Game J. 7(2):100-111.

Lauckhart, J. Burton. 1955. The effect of logging old-growth timber on bear. Proc. Soc. of Amer. For.:128-130.

Levin, Oscar R. 1954. The south Olympic tree farm. J. For. 52:243-249.

Lucci, Frank. 1960. Bear damage at the Crown-Zellerbach Neah Bay tree farm. North Olympic Peninsula Bear Control Unit Meeting, Proceedings. *In* files Washington Forest Protection Assoc., Seattle, Washington.

Lutz, H. J. 1951. Damage to trees by black bears in Alaska. J. For. 49:522-523.

Marks, Stuart A., and Albert W. Erickson. 1966. Age determination in the black bear. J. Wildl. Mgmt. 30(2):389-410.

Marshall, W. H., and R. K. Enders. 1942. The blastocyst of the marten (*Martes*). Anat. Rec., 84:306-310.

Miller, Gerrit S. Jr., and Remington Kellogg. 1955. List of North American recent mammals. United States Nat. Mus. Bull. 205. Smithsonian Institution, Washington, D.C. 954 pp.

Minutes, Washington Game Commission, June 1951. *In* files of Washington Department of Game, Olympia, Washington.

Minutes, Washington Game Commission, June 1969. *In* files of Washington Department of Game, Olympia, Washington.

Molnar, A. C., and R. G. McMinn. 1960. The origin of basal scars in the British Columbia interior white pine type. For. Chron. 49-60.

Moore, A. W. 1940. Wild animal damage to seed and seedlings on cut-over douglas-fir lands of Oregon and Washington. USDA Tech. Bull. No. 706. 28 pp.

Mundy, Keith R. D., and W. A. Fuller. 1964. Age determination in the grizzly bear. J. Wildl. Mgmt. 28(4):863-866.

Plice, Max J. 1952. Sugar versus the intuitive choice of foods by livestock. J. Range Manage. 5:69-75.

Radwan, M. A. 1969. Chemical composition of the sapwood of four tree species in relation to feeding by the black bear. For. Sci. 15(1):11-16.

——————————, and D. L. Campbell. 1968. Snowshoe hare preference for spotted catsear flowers in western Washington. J. Wildl. Mgmt. 32:104-108.

Rausch, Robert L. 1961. Notes on the black bear, *Ursus americanus* Pallus, in Alaska, with particular reference to dentition and growth. Zeitschriftfur Saugertierkunde, Bd. 26, H. 2, S.65-128.

Sauer, Peggy R. 1966a. Growth of black bears from the Adirondacks. Paper presented at the Northeast Section of the Wildl. Soc., Boston, Mass. 31 pp.

——————————. 1966b. Determining sex of black bears from the size of the lower canine tooth. N.Y. Fish and Game J. 13(2):140-145.

——————————, and Stuart Free. 1965. Age determination in black bears from sectioned canine teeth. Paper presented at the Northeast Wildl. Conf., Harrisburg, Penn. 16 pp.

——————————, ——————————, and Stephen Browne. 1966. Age determination in black bears from canine tooth sections. N.Y. Fish and Game J. 13(2):125-139.

Seal, Ulysses S., William R. Swain and Albert W. Erickson. 1967. Hematology of the Ursidae. Comp. Biochem. Physiol., 22:451-460.

Seton, Ernest Thompson. 1909. Lives of game animals. Vol II(1). Doubleday, Doran and Co., Inc. New York. 367 pp.

Shea, K. R. 1960. Deterioration—a pathological aspect of second-growth management in the Pacific Northwest. Weyerhaeuser Res. Note 28. 14 pp.

—————. 1961. Deterioration resulting from logging injury in douglas-fir and western hemlock. Weyerhaeuser For. Res. Note 36. 5 pp.

—————. 1967. Effect of artificial root and bole injuries on diameter increment of douglas-fir. Weyerhaeuser For. Paper 11. 11 pp.

Shigo, A. L., and E. vH. Larson. 1969. U.S. Forest Service Res. paper NE-127. 100 pp.

Snedecor, G. W. 1956. Statistical methods. Iowa State College Press, Ames.

Spencer, Howard E., Jr. 1955. The black bear and its status in Maine. Game Div. Bull. 4, Maine Dept. of Inland Fisheries and Game. 55 pp.

Stickley, Allen R., Jr. 1961. A black bear tagging study in Virginia. Proc. Ann. Conf. S.E. Assoc. Game and Fish Comm. 15:43-54.

Stoneberg, Ronald P., and Charles J. Jonkel. 1966. Age determination of black bears by cementum layers. J. Wildl. Mgmt. 30(2):411-414.

Svihla, Arthur, Howard Bowman and Roger Pearson. 1955. Blood picture of the American black bear, *Ursus americanus.* J. Mammal. 36(1):134-135.

Thomas D. 1967. Histological technique for bear teeth. Univ. of British Columbia. Unpubl. rpt. 3 pp.

Walker, Ernest P. 1968. Mammals of the world. Vol. II. The John Hopkins Press. Baltimore. 1500 pp.

Wimsatt, William A. 1963. Delayed implantation in the *Ursidae,* with particular reference to the black bear (*Ursus americanus* Pallus). *In* Delayed Implantation. Allen C. Enders, Ed. Univ. of Chicago Press, Chicago: 49-76.

Wright, Ernest, and Leo A. Isaac. 1956. Decay following logging injury to western hemlock, Sitka spruce, and true firs. USDA Tech. Bull. No. 1148. 34 pp.

Wright, E., A. S. Rhoads, and L. A. Isaac. 1947. Decay losses following logging injury in partially cut stands of western hemlock and Sitka spruce. The Timberman. Vol. 48(10):52-54, 72, 74, 76.

Wright, William H. 1910. The black bear. Charles Scribner's Sons, New York. 50 pp.

Youatt, W. G., and A. W. Erickson. 1958. Notes on hematology of Michigan black bears. J. Mammal. 39(4):588-589.

Zeedyk, William D. 1957. Why do bears girdle balsam fir in Maine? J. For. 55:731-732.

# APPENDIX A

# BEAR DAMAGE SURVEY QUESTIONNAIRE
## for the
# BLACK BEAR STUDY

## SECTION I

### INTRODUCTION

The increase in bear damage to timber stands during the past twenty years is recognized as a critical problem in many parts of the coastal region of the Northwest. Efforts to solve this problem by means of organized bear control programs employing paid trappers and hunters have been costly and only partially effective, except where conducted intensively over long periods of time. These programs, which have removed large numbers of bear from extensive timbered areas, have also received an increasing amount of criticism.

A study of the black bear was instigated by the Wildlife Problems Committee of the Northwest Pest Action Council to find better methods of controlling bear damage to timber. With an increased demand by the public for more recreation, it is felt that by a comprehensive study of the black bear, management techniques will be developed which will allow maximum recreational utilization of this resource in a manner compatible with the protection and operation interests of the forest industry, and at the same time control damage to timber. The study will seek information on the biology and ecology of the black bear in the coastal region of the Northwest, with emphasis on the inter-relationships of this animal and coniferous forests. A special effort will be made to determine why bears feed on the sapwood of trees by ecological, food habit, and nutritional studies. This information will be of value in determining the relationships between bear damage and forest management practices, and in finding other possible means of control.

The black bear study is being conducted by the State of Washington Department of Natural Resources, State of Washington Department of Game, Washington Forest Protection Association, Weyerhaeuser Company, U.S. Forest Service, U.S. Fish & Wildlife Service, and the College of Forestry, University of Washington. Two biologists, Douglas Pierson of the State of Washington Department of Game, and Harry Hartwell of the State of Washington Department of Natural Resources, are assigned to work full time on the project for 3 consecutive years. Donald Dickmann, a forestry student of the University of Washington, will work on the project during summer months. Western Washington was selected as the primary area of investigation. The study headquarters is located at the Forest Research Center, Olympia, Washington.

Several noteworthy characteristics of bear damage have been observed and reported, the most interesting of which are as follows: (1) Bears feed primarily on immature, smooth-barked conifers. (2) Although bears girdle various species of trees, certain species seem to be preferred. (3) Limby trees growing in open stands are more frequently damaged than trees growing in medium or well stocked stands. (4) Timber stands growing on low sites are much less susceptible to bear damage than stands growing on high sites. (5) In Western Washington, bear damage occurs only in certain areas of the vast acreage of immature timber which appears to be susceptible to damage.

The distribution of bear damage in specific areas is one of the most perplexing of the damage characteristics. The major bear damage areas in Washington are in the northern, western and southern portions of the Olympic Peninsula, the extreme southern portion of the Willapa Hills, and the foothills of the Cascades from about southern King County southward to the Yacolt Burn in Clark County and then eastward to the edge of the pine forests in Klickitat County. Although bear damage was formerly thought to be a problem confined to the coastal forests, localized areas of significant damage have been reported in Yakima, Okanogan, and Stevens Counties in Eastern Washington. One of the most interesting features of bear damage is its absence over the major portion of the Willapa Hills to the south of the Chehalis River. In contrast, to the north of this river in Grays Harbor County, bear damage has been extensive and intensive for more than a decade. Bear damage has not been reported in the northern Whatcom, Skagit, and Snohomish Counties and was apparently absent in the Black Hills (Capitol Forest area) in Thurston and Grays Harbor Counties until a small tract of new damage was discovered in 1962.

## INFORMATION REQUESTED

One of the first objectives of the study is to obtain a comprehensive knowledge of bear damage, and especially a more accurate description of damaged and undamaged areas. This questionnaire was designed to obtain such information from forest managers and other persons most intimately associated with large segments of forest land throughout Western Washington. You are one of the persons selected to complete the questionnaire. Additional field work is not required. Bear damage, as referred to in the questionnaire, consists of the removal of outer bark by bears to feed on the sapwood. It includes all trees bearing recognizable bark removal injuries, regardless of whether the trees are dead or still living. In order to obtain the maximum amount of information from the survey, you are requested to submit information on bear damage from all lands you are familiar with in your operational area. The main reasons for this are that the questionnaire is not being sent to the owners or managers of the smaller forest units and that some persons will be more familiar with bear damage than others.

If bear damage does occur in your area, you are requested to answer a list of questions concerning bear damage and also submit a map showing the location and extent of the damage, based on your observations. The details for completing these two parts are included in Section II under the headings, *Questions* and *Mapping Specifications*. If you have not observed bear damage

152

in your area, all you need to do is answer questions 1 through 5. In completing the questionnaire, we wish to emphasize that the most important objective of the survey is to obtain a comprehensive knowledge of the occurrence and distribution of bear damage. Even insignificant amounts of damage are of importance to the study.

Your cooperation in the survey will be appreciated. We would like to receive the information requested at an early date so that a progress report on the possible relationships of bear damage to certain criteria (such as timber types, soil types, fires, and reforestation), can be completed before December 31, 1963. We will need only Section II of the questionnaire form. You may keep Section I.

Return your information to:
Department of Natural Resources
Forest Research Center
Route 4, Box 424 A
Olympia, Washington

# SECTION II

### -QUESTIONS

Answer the following questions (except 1 and 2) according to your observations. If you have not observed bear damage in your area, merely answer questions 1 through 5.

1. Complete the following information:

Name and Title_____ Employer_____

Office (of home) address_____

2. Describe the general area covered by your survey, such as the name of your district or tree farm, or location according to county designation:

3. Have you observed any bear damage in your operation area?
Yes_____No_____
If your answer is "no", are you reasonably confident that bear damage does not exist in your area?     Yes_____No_____

4. If you have not observed bear damage in your area, is there any evidence that bear occur there?     Yes_____No_____

If you wish, give remarks concerning the presence or number of bear in your area.

5.   Are the timber stands in your area predominantly *saw timber* size (15 inches dbh or over for conifers other than pines; 11 inches dbh or over for pines and hardwoods), or *pole timber* size (5 to 14.9 inches for conifers other than pines; 5 to 10.9 inches dbh for pines and hardwoods)?

6.   List all of the tree species (by full common name) which you have observed damaged by bear in your area.

7.   Have you observed what appears to be a preference by bears for the sapwood of one or two tree species?        Yes_____No_____

     If your answer is "yes", list these species (in order of preference if naming two species).

8.   If known, what is the predominant age class of bear damaged trees in your area? Indicate age class by a range of 20 years (for example, 20 to 40 years).

9.   If you can give a reasonably accurate estimate, what is the average dbh of trees most frequently damaged in your area? Indicate dbh by a range of 5 inches (for example 5 to 10 inches).

10.   Have you observed any significant variation in the amount of bear damage between *poorly stocked* (10-39%), *medium stocked* (40-69%), and *well stocked* (70-100%) stands of similar species composition, size and site quality in your area?        Yes_____No_____

     If your answer is "yes", in which of these stocking classes have you observed the greatest amount of damage?

     Have you observed any significant amount of damage in well stocked stands?        Yes_____No_____

11.   Have you observed any significant variation in the amount of bear damage between stands of different site quality but of similar species composition, size, and stocking?        Yes_____No_____

     If your answer is "yes", in which sites (I, II, III, IV, V) have you observed the greatest amount of damage?

     Are there any sites in your area where bear damage is obviously negligible or absent?        Yes_____No_____

     If your answer is "yes", list these sites.

12.   If known, has the majority of bear damage in your area occurred recently, i.e. during the last 15 years?        Yes_____No_____

     Is there any evidence that damage has been occurring in your area for a much longer period of time?        Yes_____No_____

## MAPPING SPECIFICATIONS

If bear damage occurs in your operational area you are requested to submit a map or map tracing showing the known areas of damage, regardless of ownership. A sufficient number of maps are not available for distribution. If you cannot submit a map or tracing, a map can be provided upon request to the study headquarters. Maps with a scale of one-half inch to the mile or smaller are most suitable. Coordinates designating townships, ranges and sections are essential. Separate maps or tracings may be used to describe widely separated damage areas. The information received from various cooperators will be the main basis for preparing a composite map showing the distribution of bear damage in Western Washington. The following mapping procedures should be used so that the information from many sources can be interpreted *correctly*.

Step 1.  Outline the area or areas covered by your bear damage survey as accurately as possible with a solid colored line (other than red). This information is needed to determine the total area covered by the survey.

Step 2.  Outline all known areas of bear damage in the survey area with a solid red line, regardless of the amount of damage present. Do not extend the damage boundaries beyond areas where you have not actually observed damage.

Step 3.  Within the bear damage boundaries, outline with a solid black pencil line any large areas which either do not have trees or which contain trees too small to be damaged (under 4″ d.b.h.). You may indicate what these represent by such terms as "agricultural area", "burn", "blowdown", "brush area", "small reproduction", or "recent clearcut".

Step 4.  Within the bear damage areas, clearly indicate by solid red shading any portions which you consider to be heavily damaged. As a guideline, heavy damage will refer to stands in which 25% or more of the trees over 4″ d.b.h. have been damaged by bear.

# APPENDIX B

Bear damage transects described below were established in areas of extensive damage and were for collection of data concerning damage characteristics in that area. Data was collected in 1965.

## TRANSECT NUMBER 1

This stand, approximately 20 years old, was surveyed by U.S. Forest Service personnel. It is located in Section 2, Township 21 North, Range 9 West, W.M. The stand, a mixed Douglas-fir and western hemlock type, had 1457 stems per acre.

Species composition is shown in Table B-1. Data indicates that western hemlock is dominant below 6 inches dbh and Douglas-fir dominant above 6 inches dbh.

**TABLE B-1.—Coniferous species composition—Transect No. 1**

| Species | Percentage by DBH class | | | | | % of Area |
|---|---|---|---|---|---|---|
| | 1-2" | 3-4" | 5-6" | 7-8" | 9-10" | |
| Douglas-fir | 2 | 11 | 42 | 62 | 51 | 15 |
| Hemlock | 98 | 89 | 58 | 38 | 49 | 85 |
| % of area | 50 | 27 | 15 | 6 | 2 | |

Bear damage, both injured and killed, is shown in Table B-2. Bear damage to western hemlock is low up to the 9 to 10 inch dbh class, where 48 percent were found to be damaged. Douglas-fir sustained considerable damage from the 5 to 6 inch dbh class and larger. Ninety-one percent of the 9 to 10 inch dbh Douglas-fir were damaged. Seven percent of the total stand was damaged.

**TABLE B-2.—Bear damage[a]—Transect No. 1**

| Species | DBH | | | | | |
|---|---|---|---|---|---|---|
| | 1-2" | 3-4" | 5-6" | 7-8" | 9-10" | |
| | % Damaged by Spp/Cl[b] | % Damaged by Spp/Cl | % Damaged by Spp/Cl | % Damaged by Spp/Cl | % Damaged by Spp/Cl | % total damage Spp/Area |
| Douglas-fir | 0/0 | 11/100 | 43/95 | 77/95 | 91/67 | 44/90 |
| Hemlock | 0/0 | 0/0 | 2/5 | 6/5 | 48/33 | 1/10 |
| Area totals | | 1/5 | 19/39 | 50/42 | 70/14 | 7/100 |

[a]Both injured and killed trees.
[b]Species/class.

When species availability (percent of species in class) is compared to percent of damage in the class, it is found that Douglas-fir sustains the majority of damage in all dbh classes. Douglas-fir composes 15 percent of the stand and sustains 90 percent of the damage (Table B-3).

TABLE B-3.—Species composition compared to total damage—Transect No. 1

| Species | DBH | | | | | |
| | 1-2″ | 3-4″ | 5-6″ | 7-8″ | 9-10″ | |
| | % Cl/Dam | % Cl/Dam | % Cl/Dam | % Cl/Dam | % Cl/Dam | Total % of Area/Damage |
|---|---|---|---|---|---|---|
| Douglas-fir | 2/0[a] | 11/100 | 42/95 | 62/95 | 51/67 | 15/90[b] |
| Hemlock | 98/0 | 89/0 | 58/5 | 38/5 | 49/33 | 85/10 |
| Area totals | 50/0 | 27/5 | 15/39 | 6/42 | 2/14 | 100/7[c] |

[a]Species composition/damage within dbh class.
[b]Species composition/damage within stand.
[c]% of total stand damaged.

Data from this table are used to compute species preference ratings. Douglas-fir was used as the base species in determination of preference ratings for all transects described in this appendix.

Preference ratings show Douglas-fir as the preferred species (Table B-4).

TABLE B-4.—Preference ratings—Transect No. 1

| Species | Preference rating by DBH class | | | | Area preference rating |
| | 3-4″ | 5-6″ | 7-8″ | 9-10″ | |
|---|---|---|---|---|---|
| Douglas-fir | 100 | 100 | 100 | 100 | 100 |
| Hemlock | 0 | 4 | 8 | 51 | 2 |

## TRANSECT NUMBER 2

This stand was surveyed by West Tacoma Newsprint personnel in connection with their regular forest inventory. The stand is located in Township 21 North, Range 9 West, W.M., and Township 19 North, Range 10 West, W.M. Species composition, bear damage and preference ratings are shown in Tables B-5, B-6, B-7.

158

**TABLE B-5.—Species composition—Transect No. 2**

| Species | Percentage by DBH class | | | | | % of Area |
|---|---|---|---|---|---|---|
| | 5-10″ | 11-15″ | 16-20″ | 21-25″ | Over 25″ | |
| Douglas-fir | 8 | 20 | 41 | 37 | 17 | 22 |
| Hemlock | 67 | 63 | 50 | 58 | 69 | 61 |
| Cedar | 13 | 5 | 2 | 1 | 1 | 7 |
| Spruce | 1 | 1 | 2 | 2 | 10 | 2 |
| Red alder | 11 | 10 | 5 | 1 | 2 | 8 |
| % of area | 31 | 38 | 20 | 7 | 4 | |

**TABLE B-6.—Species composition compared to total damage[a]—Transect No. 2**

| Species | DBH | | | | | Total % of Area/Damage |
|---|---|---|---|---|---|---|
| | 5-10″ | 11-15″ | 16-20″ | 21-25″ | Over 25″ | |
| | % Cl/Dam | % Cl/Dam | % Cl/Dam | % Cl/Dam | % Cl/Dam | |
| Douglas-fir | 8/13[b] | 20/23 | 41/47 | 37/60 | 17/67 | 22/32[c] |
| Hemlock | 67/45 | 63/61 | 50/47 | 58/38 | 69/33 | 61/52 |
| Cedar | 13/42 | 5/16 | 2/6 | 1/2 | 1/0 | 7/16 |
| Spruce | 1/0 | 1/0 | 2/0 | 2/0 | 10/0 | 2/0 |
| Red alder | 11/0 | 10/0 | 5/0 | 1/0 | 2/0 | 8/0 |
| Area totals | 31/14 | 38/47 | 20/30 | 7/8 | 4/1 | 100/100[d] |

[a]Both injured and killed trees.
[b]Species composition/damage within dbh class.
[c]Species composition/damage within stand.
[d]% of total stand damaged.

**TABLE B-7.—Preference ratings—Transect No. 2**

| Species | Preference rating by DBH class | | | | | Area preference rating |
|---|---|---|---|---|---|---|
| | 5-10″ | 11-15″ | 16-20″ | 21-25″ | Over 25″ | |
| Douglas-fir | 100 | 100 | 100 | 100 | 100 | 100 |
| Hemlock | 41 | 84 | 82 | 41 | 12 | 59 |
| Cedar | 198 | 278 | 261 | 123 | 0 | 157 |

Big leaf maple, western white fir and black cottonwood were found in the inventory area but had sustained no bear damage.

Species preference ratings show cedar as the preferred species in all dbh classes. Douglas-fir is second, followed by hemlock.

159

## TRANSECT NUMBER 3

This 40-45 year-old stand was located in the SE ¼, Section 20, Township 11 North, Range 8 East, W.M. Principal understory species were salal (*Gaultheria shallon*), bracken fern (*Pteridium aquilinum pubescens*) and Devil's Club (*Oplopanax horridus*). Site class was a low III or high IV. Elevation was about 2,900 feet. The majority of the damage had occurred since 1959.

Douglas-fir and western hemlock made up 75 percent of the stand, with the remainder being western redcedar, red alder and other hardwood species (Table B-8). The majority of the trees were below 15 inches dbh.

TABLE B-8.—Species composition—Transect No. 3

| Species | Percentage By DBH class | | | | |
| | 5-10" | 11-15" | 16-20" | 21-25" | % of Area |
|---|---|---|---|---|---|
| Douglas-fir | 43 | 65 | 86 | 67 | 52 |
| Hemlock | 30 | 14 | 7 | 0 | 23 |
| Red alder | 10 | 8 | 0 | 0 | 9 |
| Black cottonwood | 2 | 1 | 0 | 33 | 2 |
| Vine maple | 7 | 0 | 0 | 0 | 5 |
| Cedar | 7 | 12 | 7 | 0 | 8 |
| Cherry | 1 | 0 | 0 | 0 | 1 |
| % of area | 66 | 25 | 7 | 2 | |

Bear damage, both injured and killed, is shown in Table B-9 by species and dbh class. Douglas-fir received 67 percent of the total damage, with 35 percent of the species damaged. The interesting damage characteristic indicated by this table is the damage to red alder and black cottonwood. Twenty-seven percent of the stand was damaged. The majority of the damage was in the 11 to 15 inch dbh class.

Table B-10 is a combination of Tables B-8 and B-9 and allows a comparison of class characteristics by species. Douglas-fir makes up the largest percent in each dbh class and sustains the greatest percent of the damage in each class. Western hemlock and western redcedar are next in percent of damage.

Preference ratings are shown in Table B-11.

When availability of all species is made comparable, it is found that although Douglas-fir sustains the majority of the damage, it is not the preferred species. Black cottonwood and western redcedar are more preferred than Douglas-fir and western hemlock.

160

**TABLE B-9.—Bear damage[a]—Transect No. 3**

| Species | DBH | | | |
| | 5-10" | 11-15" | 16-20" | |
| | % Damaged by Spp/Cl[b] | % Damaged by Spp/Cl | % Damaged by Spp/Cl | % Total damage Spp/Area |
|---|---|---|---|---|
| Douglas-fir | 25/64 | 52/63 | 46/100 | 35/67 |
| Hemlock | 10/18 | 57/15 | 0/0 | 17/14 |
| Red alder | 7/5 | 25/4 | 0/0 | 11/4 |
| Black cottonwood | 67/8 | 0/0 | 0/0 | 40/4 |
| Vine maple | 0/0 | 0/0 | 0/0 | 0/0 |
| Cedar | 11/5 | 84/18 | 0/0 | 38/11 |
| Cherry | 0/0 | 0/0 | 0/0 | 0/0 |
| Area totals | 16/40 | 53/49 | 33/11 | 27/100 |

[a]Both injured and killed trees.
[b]Species/class.

**TABLE B-10.—Species composition compared to total damage—Transect No. 3**

| Species | DBH | | | | |
| | 5-10" | 11-15" | 16-20" | 21-25" | |
| | % Cl/Dam | % Cl/Dam | % Cl/Dam | % Cl/Dam | Total % of Area/Damage |
|---|---|---|---|---|---|
| Douglas-fir | 43/64[a] | 65/63 | 86/100 | 67/0 | 52/67[b] |
| Hemlock | 30/18 | 14/15 | 7/0 | 0/0 | 23/14 |
| Red alder | 10/5 | 8/4 | 0/0 | 0/0 | 9/4 |
| Black cottonwood | 2/8 | 1/0 | 0/0 | 33/0 | 2/4 |
| Vine maple | 7/0 | 0/0 | 0/0 | 0/0 | 5/0 |
| Cedar | 7/5 | 12/18 | 7/0 | 0/0 | 8/11 |
| Cherry | 1/0 | 0/0 | 0/0 | 0/0 | 1/0 |
| Area totals | 66/40 | 25/49 | 7/11 | 2/0 | 100/27[c] |

[a]Species composition/damage within dbh class.
[b]Species composition/damage within stand.
[c]% of total stand damaged.

**TABLE B-11.—Preference ratings—Transect No. 3**

| Species | Preference rating by DBH class | | | Area preference rating |
| | 5-10" | 11-15" | 16-20" | |
|---|---|---|---|---|
| Douglas-fir | 100 | 100 | 100 | 100 |
| Hemlock | 40 | 111 | 0 | 47 |
| Red alder | 34 | 52 | 0 | 34 |
| Black cottonwood | 269 | 0 | 0 | 155 |
| Cedar | 48 | 155 | . . . | 107 |

## TRANSECT NUMBER 4

This transect was located in a virgin stand of mountain hemlock and Pacific silver fir growing on rocky soil at an elevation of approximately 5,650 feet in the NW ¼, Section 6, Township 10 North, Range 10 East, W.M. Damage was basal in nearly all cases.

Species composition, bear damage and species preferences are shown in Tables B-12, B-13, B-14 and B-15.

**TABLE B-12.—Coniferous species composition—Transect No. 4**

| Species | Pecentage by DBH class | | | | % of Area |
|---|---|---|---|---|---|
| | 5-10" | 11-15" | 16-20" | 21-25" | |
| Silver fir | 76 | 95 | 80 | 50 | 81 |
| Mt. Hemlock | 24 | 5 | 20 | 50 | 19 |
| % of area | 68 | 23 | 8 | 1 | |

**TABLE B-13.—Bear damage[a]—Transect No. 4**

| Species | DBH | | | | |
|---|---|---|---|---|---|
| | 5-10" | 11-15" | 16-20" | 21-25" | |
| | % Damaged by Spp/Cl[b] | % Damaged by Spp/Cl | % Damaged by Spp/Cl | % Damaged by Spp/Cl | % Total damage Spp/Area |
| Silver Fir | 20/80 | 55/100 | 42/100 | 0/0 | 31/89 |
| Mt. Hemlock | 17/20 | 0/0 | 0/0 | 100/100 | 17/11 |
| Area totals | 20/47 | 52/42 | 33/9 | 50/2 | 28/100 |

[a]Both injured and killed trees.
[c]Species/Class.

**TABLE B-14.—Species composition compared to total damage—Transect No. 4**

| Species | DBH | | | | |
|---|---|---|---|---|---|
| | 5-10" | 11-15" | 16-20" | 21-25" | |
| | % Cl/Dam | % Cl/Dam | % Cl/Dam | % Cl/Dam | Total % of Area/Damage |
| Silver fir | 76/80[a] | 95/100 | 80/100 | 50/0 | 81/89[b] |
| Mt. Hemlock | 24/20 | 5/0 | 20/0 | 50/100 | 19/11 |
| Area totals | 68/47 | 23/42 | 8/9 | 1/2 | 100/28[c] |

[a]Species composition/damage within dbh class.
[b]Species composition/damage within stand.
[c]% of total stand damaged.

162

**TABLE B-15.—Preference ratings—Transect No. 4**

| Species | Preference rating by DBH class | | | | Area preference rating |
|---|---|---|---|---|---|
| | 5-10" | 11-15" | 16-20" | 21-25" | |
| Silver fir | 100 | 100 | 100 | 0 | 100 |
| Mt. Hemlock | 80 | 0 | 0 | 100 | 44 |

The majority of the damage, both injured and killed, occurred in Pacific silver fir, with the 11 to 15 inch dbh class sustaining the highest percent of class damage. Mountain hemlock sustained damage in the 5 to 10 inch and 21 to 25 inch dbh classes. Twenty-eight percent of the trees measured had been damaged, and the majority of the damage was in the 5 to 10 inch dbh class. Pacific silver fir was the preferred species.

## TRANSECT NUMBER 5

This transect was located in the SE ¼, Section 36, Township 11 North, Range 8 East, W.M., and the NE ¼, Section 35, Township 11 North, Range 8 East. W.M. The stand was a mixed Douglas-fir, western hemlock, Pacific silver fir type growing on rocky soil at 4,600 feet elevation with bracken fern understory. The stand had been burned approximately 60 years ago. Most bear damage was basal.

**TABLE B-16.—Coniferous species composition—Transect No. 5**

| Species | Percentage by DBH class | | | % of Area |
|---|---|---|---|---|
| | 5-10" | 11-15" | 16-20" | |
| Douglas-fir | 53 | 61 | 75 | 55 |
| Silver fir | 20 | 28 | 25 | 21 |
| Hemlock | 25 | 11 | 0 | 22 |
| Engelmann spruce | 2 | 0 | 0 | 2 |
| % of area | 82 | 15 | 3 | |

Douglas-fir was the dominant species. The majority of the stand was below 10 inches dbh, and no trees were above 20 inches dbh.

The majority of damage occurred in Douglas-fir. Fifty-four percent of all Douglas-fir were damaged, and this damage represented 88 percent of the total transect damage. Engelmann spruce contributed only 5 percent of the total damage, but all of the Engelmann spruce in the transect were damaged. Hemlock was not damaged. The majority of damage was in the 5 to 10 inch dbh class and 34 percent of the stand was damaged (Table B-17).

163

Preference ratings calculated from data in Table B-18 show Engelmann spruce as the preferred species, followed by Douglas-fir and silver fir (Table B-19).

**TABLE B-17.—Bear damage[a]—Transect No. 5**

| | DBH | | | |
| | 5-10" | 11-15" | 16-20" | |
| Species | % Damaged by Spp/Cl[b] | % Damaged by Spp/Cl | % Damaged by Spp/Cl | % Total damage Spp/Area |
|---|---|---|---|---|
| Douglas-fir | 51/90 | 64/78 | 67/100 | 54/88 |
| Silver fir | 5/3 | 40/12 | 0/0 | 12/7 |
| Hemlock | 0/0 | 0/0 | 0/0 | 0/0 |
| Engelmann spruce | 100/7 | 0/0 | 0/0 | 100/5 |
| Area totals | 30/73 | 50/22 | 50/5 | 34/100 |

[a]Both injured and killed trees.
[b]Species/class.

**TABLE B-18.—Species composition compared to total damage—Transect No. 5**

| | DBH | | | |
| | 5-10" | 11-15" | 16-20" | |
| Species | % Cl/Dam | % Cl/Dam | % Cl/Dam | Total % of Area/Damage |
|---|---|---|---|---|
| Douglas-fir | 53/90[a] | 61/78 | 75/100 | 55/88[b] |
| Silver fir | 20/3 | 28/12 | 25/0 | 21/7 |
| Hemlock | 25/0 | 11/0 | 0/0 | 22/0 |
| Engelmann spruce | 2/7 | 0/0 | 0/0 | 2/5 |
| Area totals | 82/73 | 15/22 | 3/5 | 100/34[c] |

[a]Species composition/damage within dbh class.
[b]Species composition/damage within stand.
[c]% of total stand damaged.

**TABLE B-19.—Preference ratings—Transect No. 5**

| | Preference rating by DBH class | | | Area preference rating |
| Species | 5-10" | 11-15" | 16-20" | |
|---|---|---|---|---|
| Douglas-fir | 100 | 100 | 100 | 100 |
| Silver fir | 9 | 34 | 0 | 21 |
| Hemlock | 0 | 0 | 0 | 0 |
| Engelmann spruce | 206 | 0 | 0 | 156 |

## TRANSECT NUMBER 6

Transect Number 6 was located in the SE ¼, Section 36, Township 12 North, Range 8 East, W.M. and S ½, Section 31, Township 12 North, Range 9 East, W.M. The stand was a Pacific silver fir and mountain hemlock type, 150-250 years old, 5,600 feet in elevation, with blue huckleberry (*vaccinium deliciosum*) understory. Site category was a low V. Bear damage was basal.

Species composition shows Pacific silver fir and mountain hemlock as dominant species with noble fir and grand fir present (Table B-20).

**TABLE B-20.—Coniferous species composition—Transect No. 6**

| Species | Percentage by DBH class | | | | | % of Area |
|---|---|---|---|---|---|---|
| | 5-10" | 11-15" | 16-20" | 21-25" | Over 25" | |
| Silver fir | 69 | 66 | 50 | 71 | 65 | 64 |
| Mt. Hemlock | 30 | 31 | 50 | 21 | 23 | 33 |
| Noble fir | 0 | 3 | 0 | 8 | 6 | 2 |
| Grand fir | 1 | 0 | 0 | 0 | 6 | 1 |
| % of area | 53 | 13 | 19 | 7 | 8 | |

Data in Table B-21 shows that Pacific silver fir sustained the majority of damage. Mountain hemlock was second in terms of total trees damaged followed by noble fir. No damage to grand fir was recorded. The majority of damage was in the 16 to 20-inch dbh class and 28 percent of the stand was damaged.

**TABLE B-21.—Bear damage[a]—Transect No. 6**

| Species | DBH | | | | | |
|---|---|---|---|---|---|---|
| | 5-10" | 11-15" | 16-20" | 21-25" | Over 25" | |
| | % Damaged by Spp/Cl[b] | % Damaged by Spp/Cl | % Damaged by Spp/Cl | % Damaged by Spp/Cl | % Damaged by Spp/Cl | % Total damage Spp/Area |
| Silver fir | 14/55 | 37/70 | 55/52 | 40/68 | 36/100 | 27/61 |
| Mt. Hemlock | 26/45 | 22/20 | 50/53 | 33/16 | 0/0 | 31/36 |
| Noble fir | 0/0 | 100/10 | 0/0 | 100/16 | 0/0 | 67/3 |
| Grand fir | 0/0 | 0/0 | 0/0 | 0/0 | 0/0 | 0/0 |
| Area totals | 17/33 | 34/16 | 53/34 | 43/10 | 24/7 | 28/100 |

[a]Both injured and killed trees.
[b]Species/class.

Percent of species in the class compared to percent of class damage indicates Pacific silver fir sustained the greatest amount of damage, in terms of percent of total stand damage, followed by mountain hemlock and noble fir (Table B-22).

**TABLE B-22.—Species composition compared to total damage—Transect No. 6**

| | DBH | | | | | |
| | 5-10″ | 11-15″ | 16-20″ | 21-25″ | Over 25″ | |
| Species | %<br>Cl/Dam | %<br>Cl/Dam | %<br>Cl/Dam | %<br>Cl/Dam | %<br>Cl/Dam | Total % of<br>Area/Damage |
|---|---|---|---|---|---|---|
| Silver fir | 69/55[a] | 66/70 | 50/52 | 71/68 | 65/100 | 64/61[b] |
| Mt. Hemlock | 30/45 | 31/20 | 50/53 | 21/16 | 23/0 | 33/36 |
| Noble fir | 0/0 | 3/10 | 0/0 | 8/16 | 6/0 | 2/3 |
| Grand fir | 1/0 | 0/0 | 0/0 | 0/0 | 6/0 | 1/0 |
| Area totals | 53/33 | 13/16 | 19/34 | 7/10 | 8/7 | 100/28[c] |

[a]Species composition/damage within dbh class.
[b]Species composition/damage within stand.
[c]% of total stand damaged.

Preference ratings show noble fir is preferred, followed by mountain hemlock and Pacific silver fir (Table B-23).

**TABLE B-23.—Preference ratings—Transect No. 6**

| | Preference rating<br>by DBH class | | | | | Area<br>preference<br>rating |
| Species | 5-10″ | 11-15″ | 16-20″ | 21-25″ | Over 25″ | |
|---|---|---|---|---|---|---|
| Silver fir | 100 | 100 | 100 | 100 | 100 | 100 |
| Mt. Hemlock | 187 | 61 | 102 | 79 | 0 | 115 |
| Noble fir | 0 | 314 | 0 | 208 | 0 | 158 |

## TRANSECT NUMBER 7

This transect was located in the SE ¼, Section 11, Township 7 North, Range 11 East, W.M. The transect was located on a rocky site and had an understory of small conifer reproduction and grasses. The area had never been logged, but had burned 60-100 years ago.

Species composition shows lodgepole pine dominant, with the majority of the stand below 10 inches dbh (Table B-24).

**TABLE B-24.—Coniferous species composition—Transect No. 7**

| | Percentage by<br>DBH class | | | | | |
| Species | 5-10″ | 11-15″ | 16-20″ | 21-25″ | Over 25″ | % of Area |
|---|---|---|---|---|---|---|
| Lodgepole pine | 90 | 61 | 0 | 0 | 0 | 82 |
| Ponderosa pine | 8 | 36 | 100 | 100 | 100 | 16 |
| White fir | 2 | 3 | 0 | 0 | 0 | |
| % of area | 77 | 20 | 1 | 1 | 1 | |

Bear damage data indicate that lodgepole pine is the preferred species. Eleven percent of the lodgepole pine in the stand were damaged. Sixty-two percent of the damage was in the 5 to 10 inch dbh class (Table B-25).

**TABLE B-25.—Bear damage[a]—Transect No. 7**

| | DBH | | |
| | 5-10″ | 11-15″ | |
| Species | % Damage by Species/Class | % Damage by Species/Class | % Total Damage Species/Area |
|---|---|---|---|
| | % Damage by | % Damage by | % Total damage |
| Lodgepole pine | 8/100 | 29/100 | 11/100 |
| Area totals | 7/62 | 18/38 | 9/100 |

[a]Both injured and killed trees.

## TRANSECT NUMBER 8

Transect Number 8 was measured in the SW ¼, Section 17, Township 7 North, Range 11 East, W.M. The stand was on rocky soil and had burned 60-100 years ago but had never been logged. Understory was primarily lodgepole and white fir reproduction, with some grasses. The stand was primarily lodgepole pine under 10 inches dbh (Table B-26).

**TABLE B-26.—Coniferous species composition—Transect No. 8**

| | Percentage by DBH class | | | | | |
|---|---|---|---|---|---|---|
| Species | 5-10″ | 11-15″ | 16-20″ | 21-25″ | Over 25″ | % of Area |
| Lodgepole pine | 83 | 98 | 100 | 33 | 0 | 84 |
| White fir | 15 | 2 | 0 | 0 | 0 | 12 |
| Ponderosa pine | 2 | 0 | 0 | 67 | 100 | 4 |
| % of area | 82 | 14 | 2 | 1 | 1 | |

Bear damage data shows lodgepole pine as the preferred species, with 14 percent damaged. No damage was recorded to either white fir or ponderosa pine. Eighty-two percent of the damage was in the 5 to 10-inch dbh class (Table B-27).

## TRANSECT NUMBER 9

Located in the NW ¼, Section 9, Township 6 North, Range 9 East, W.M., this transect was in a mixed stand of several species. Although never logged, the area had burned sometime previously. Elevation was approximately 3,800 feet. Bear damage was found mainly in swampy creek bottom areas. Engelmann spruce was the dominant species. The majority of the stand was below 10 inches dbh (Table B-28).

167

**TABLE B-27.—Bear damage[a]—Transect No. 8**

| | DBH | | | | |
|---|---|---|---|---|---|
| | 5-10″ | 11-15″ | 16-20″ | Over 25″ | |
| Species | % Damaged by Spp/Cl[b] | % Damaged by Spp/Cl | % Damaged by Spp/Cl | % Damaged by Spp/Cl | % Total damage Spp/Area |
| Lodgepole pine | 12/100 | 17/100 | 50/100 | 100/100 | 14/100 |
| Area totals | 10/70 | 17/21 | 50/6 | 33/3 | 12/100 |

[a]Both injured and killed trees.
[b]Species/class.

**TABLE B-28.—Species composition—Transect No. 9**

| | Percentage by DBH class | | | | | |
|---|---|---|---|---|---|---|
| Species | 5-10″ | 11-15″ | 16-20″ | 21-25″ | Over 25″ | % of Area |
| Engelmann spruce | 42 | 48 | 29 | 67 | 50 | 43 |
| White fir | 9 | 3 | 14 | 0 | 0 | 8 |
| Western hemlock | 7 | 0 | 0 | 0 | 0 | 5 |
| Douglas-fir | 2 | 26 | 43 | 0 | 50 | 11 |
| Black cottonwood | 2 | 3 | 0 | 0 | 0 | 2 |
| White pine | 16 | 13 | 14 | 33 | 0 | 15 |
| Western larch | 1 | 0 | 0 | 0 | 0 | 1 |
| Lodgepole pine | 16 | 7 | 0 | 0 | 0 | 12 |
| Mt. Hemlock | 4 | 0 | 0 | 0 | 0 | 2 |
| Cedar | 1 | 0 | 0 | 0 | 0 | 1 |
| % of area | 67 | 24 | 5 | 2 | 2 | |

**TABLE B-29.—Bear damage[a]—Transect No. 9**

| | DBH | | | | |
|---|---|---|---|---|---|
| | 5-10″ | 11-15″ | 16-20″ | Over 25″ | |
| Species | % Damaged by Spp/Cl[b] | % Damaged by Spp/Cl | % Damaged by Spp/Cl | % Damaged by Spp/Cl | % Total Damage Spp/Area |
| Engelmann spruce | 30/44 | 60/64 | 0/0 | 0/0 | 39/48 |
| White fir | 0/0 | 100/7 | 100/50 | 0/0 | 100/5 |
| Douglas-fir | 0/0 | 13/7 | 0/0 | 100/100 | 22/5 |
| White pine | 71/40 | 75/21 | 100/50 | 0/0 | 74/33 |
| Lodgepole pine | 21/12 | 0/0 | 0/0 | 0/0 | 21/7 |
| Western larch | 100/4 | 0/0 | 0/0 | 0/0 | 100/2 |
| Area totals | 28/60 | 45/33 | 29/5 | 50/2 | 32/100 |

[a]Both injured and killed trees.
[b]Species/class.

Engelmann spruce sustained 48 percent of the total damage, with 39 percent of the species damaged. One-hundred percent of the white fir and western larch were damaged. Twenty-two percent of the Douglas-fir were damaged. The majority of damage occurred in the 5 to 10-inch dbh class, and 32 percent of the stand was damaged (Table B-29).

Comparison of availability and damage by dbh class shows Engelmann spruce sustaining the greatest percent of stand damage, followed by western white pine and lodgepole pine (Table B-30).

Western white pine is the preferred species, followed by western larch and Engelmann spruce (Table B-31).

**TABLE B-30.—Species composition compared to total damage—Transect No. 9**

| | DBH | | | | | |
| | 5-10" | 11-15" | 16-20" | 21-25" | Over 25" | |
| Species | % Cl/Dam | % Cl/Dam | % Cl/Dam | % Cl/Dam | % Cl/Dam | Total % of Area/Damage |
|---|---|---|---|---|---|---|
| Engelmann spruce | 42/44[a] | 48/64 | 29/0 | 67/0 | 50/0 | 43/48[b] |
| White fir | 9/0 | 3/7 | 14/50 | 0/0 | 0/0 | 8/5 |
| Douglas-fir | 2/0 | 26/7 | 43/0 | 0/0 | 50/100 | 11/5 |
| White pine | 16/40 | 13/21 | 14/50 | 33/0 | 0/0 | 25/33 |
| Western larch | 1/4 | 0/0 | 0/0 | 0/0 | 0/0 | 1/2 |
| Lodgepole pine | 16/12 | 7/0 | 0/0 | 0/0 | 0/0 | 12/7 |
| Area totals | 67/60 | 24/33 | 5/5 | 2/0 | 2/2 | 100/32[c] |

**TABLE B-31.—Preference rating—Transect No. 9**

| | Preference ratings by DBH class | | | | Area preference rating |
| Species | 5-10" | 11-15" | 16-20" | Over 25" | |
|---|---|---|---|---|---|
| Engelmann spruce | 42 | 82 | 0 | 0 | 51 |
| White fir | 0 | 144 | 100 | 0 | 29 |
| Douglas-fir | 0 | 17 | 0 | 100 | 20 |
| White pine | 100 | 100 | 100 | 0 | 100 |
| Western larch | 160 | 0 | 0 | 0 | 80 |
| Lodgepole pine | 30 | 0 | 0 | 0 | 23 |

Summary of preference ratings for Transects 1 through 9 is provided in Table 20.

# APPENDIX C

APPENDIX C

# WASHINGTON FOREST PROTECTION ASSOCIATION

The Washington Forest Protection Association was established in 1908 by a group of private forestland owners concerned with the heavy losses to forest fires each summer. During these early days, prior to the organized efforts of public forest protection agencies, the Association fielded fire suppression crews to combat this common enemy.

Throughout its history, the Association has advocated stringent laws designed to prevent forest fires from occurring and being prepared for suppressing them when they do occur.

In 1958 the old Washington Forest Fire Association was renamed the Washington Forest Protection Association and new areas of activity were directed at the "people problems" which were becoming more commonplace as populations increased and forest uses expanded. Today, the Association serves as the spokesman for the private and municipal forestland owners in Washington State on matters relating to forest taxation, governmental affairs, forest protection, land use, and public information. The organization represents approximately 55% of the total privately owned forestland in Washington State. Its members consist of the small landowner owning 10 acres of forestland to the large industrial forestland owners.

In many instances, it is of common benefit to forestland owners to join cooperatively in sponsoring certain activities which can be done more efficiently and effectively on a cooperative basis. To meet such needs, the association organizes and implements such programs as the Cooperative Helicopter Availability Program. This program provides helicopters to its members for administrative purposes, a coordinated forest fire-fighting helicopter capability which, in cooperation with the Department of Natural Resources, locates large water dumping helicopters in strategic locations throughout the state during the fire season and special forest patrols in areas of high fire danger. Animal damage control service is provided to meet the problems of predation by wild animals. Special training in forest fire suppression techniques for logging crews, organizing cooperative contract research in high priority problem areas, and providing a cooperative hunter map program as well as other activities as widely varied as those mentioned, are all part of the WFPA's function.

The Association works closely with the Washington State Department of Natural Resources and Washington State Game Department in areas of common interest. Public agencies and the news media recognize the Association as a means by which effective communications can be had with the forestland owners in Washington State.

The Association has a permanent staff of five professional persons headquartered in Seattle. Supporting staff members and other permanent and part-time personnel total approximately 30 to 40. The strength of the Association's efforts are founded in its enthusiastic membership support which attracts literally hundreds of manhours of effort expended by the principals and technical experts that are employed by the forestland owner.

The Association's motto, "working together to achieve common goals", is exemplified in the long list of significant accomplishments that have been achieved over the last 60 and more years by the forestland owners as they worked together to solve common problems.

# APPENDIX D

# BLACK BEAR DAMAGE TRANSECT

Transect No.:........................

Date: ................................

**Transect Description:**

Location: Sub............ Section ................ Township................ Range................

Soil: .............................................................................................................

Forest Type: ....................................................................................................

Understory: ......................................................................................................

Stand Age: ......................................................... Stocking Class: ....................

Land-Use & Fire History: ....................................................................................

......................................................................................................................

Notes: ............................................................................................................

......................................................................................................................

......................................................................................................................

## BLACK BEAR DAMAGE TRANSECT DATA

Species: ............................ Transect No.: .................. Date: ....................

| D.B.H. | 0-25% | 26-50% | 51-75% | 75%+ | Dead | No Damage | Total Trees |
|---|---|---|---|---|---|---|---|
| Over 25″ | | | | | | | |
| 21-25″ | | | | | | | |
| 16-20″ | | | | | | | |
| 11-15″ | | | | | | | |
| 5-10″ | | | | | | | |

**D.B.H.**                   **Degree of Girdle**

Notes: ............................................................................................................

......................................................................................................................

......................................................................................................................

Recorded by: ....................................................

# BLACK BEAR DAMAGE TRANSECT DATA

Transect No.: ........................

Date: ........................

Species ........................................................................

| | 0-25% | 26-50% | 51-75% | 75%+ | Dead | No Damage | Total Trees |
|---|---|---|---|---|---|---|---|
| Over 25″ | | | | | | | |
| 21-25″ | | | | | | | |
| 16-20″ | | | | | | | |
| 11-15″ | | | | | | | |
| 5-10″ | | | | | | | |

Species ........................................................................

| | 0-25% | 26-50% | 51-75% | 75%+ | Dead | No Damage | Total Trees |
|---|---|---|---|---|---|---|---|
| Over 25″ | | | | | | | |
| 21-25″ | | | | | | | |
| 16-20″ | | | | | | | |
| 11-15″ | | | | | | | |
| 5-10″ | | | | | | | |

Species ........................................................................

| | 0-25% | 26-50% | 51-75% | 75%+ | Dead | No Damage | Total Trees |
|---|---|---|---|---|---|---|---|
| Over 25″ | | | | | | | |
| 21-25″ | | | | | | | |
| 16-20″ | | | | | | | |
| 11-15″ | | | | | | | |
| 5-10″ | | | | | | | |

Recorded by: ........................................................................

# BEAR DAMAGE—DETERIORATION STUDIES

Transect: ‗‗‗‗‗‗‗‗‗‗‗‗‗‗‗‗‗‗‗‗‗‗‗‗‗

Plot: ‗‗‗‗‗‗‗‗‗‗‗‗‗‗‗‗‗‗‗‗‗‗‗‗‗ Date: ‗‗‗‗‗‗‗‗‗‗‗‗‗‗‗‗‗‗‗‗

Species: ‗‗‗‗‗‗‗‗‗‗‗‗‗‗‗‗‗‗‗‗‗

**Degree of Injury**

1. Percent of bole girdled: ‗‗‗‗‗‗‗‗‗‗‗‗‗‗‗‗

2. Total area (square inches): ‗‗‗‗‗‗‗‗‗‗‗‗

3. Location on trunk: ‗‗‗‗‗‗‗‗‗‗‗‗‗‗‗‗

**Age of Injury**

1. Age at time of injury:‗‗‗‗‗‗‗‗‗‗‗‗‗‗‗‗

2. Age at time of inspection:‗‗‗‗‗‗‗‗‗‗‗ Difference: ‗‗‗‗‗‗‗‗‗‗‗‗‗‗

3. D.B.H. at time of injury: ‗‗‗‗‗‗‗‗‗‗‗‗

4. D.B.H. at time of inspection: ‗‗‗‗‗‗‗‗ Difference: ‗‗‗‗‗‗‗‗‗‗‗‗‗‗

**Butt Rot & Insect Invasion**

1. Butt rot: ‗‗‗‗‗‗‗‗‗‗‗‗‗‗‗‗‗‗‗‗‗‗‗‗‗

   (a) Description of rot: ‗‗‗‗‗‗‗‗‗‗‗‗‗‗‗‗‗‗‗‗‗‗‗‗‗

2. Insect invasion: ‗‗‗‗‗‗‗‗‗‗‗‗‗‗‗‗‗‗

   (a) Description of insect: ‗‗‗‗‗‗‗‗‗‗‗‗‗‗‗‗‗‗‗‗‗‗‗‗‗

**Injury Healing**

1. Stage of healing: ‗‗‗‗‗‗‗‗‗‗‗‗‗‗‗‗‗‗‗‗‗‗‗‗‗

2. Scar tissue development: ‗‗‗‗‗‗‗‗‗‗‗‗‗‗‗‗‗‗‗‗‗‗‗‗‗

**Deterioration**

1. Total board feet: ‗‗‗‗‗‗‗‗‗‗‗‗‗‗‗‗

2. Loss due to cull: ‗‗‗‗‗‗‗‗‗‗‗‗‗‗‗‗

3. Merchantable board feet: ‗‗‗‗‗‗‗‗‗‗‗‗‗‗‗‗

Remarks: ‗‗‗‗‗‗‗‗‗‗‗‗‗‗‗‗‗‗‗‗‗‗‗‗‗‗‗‗‗‗‗‗‗‗‗‗‗‗

‗‗‗‗‗‗‗‗‗‗‗‗‗‗‗‗‗‗‗‗‗‗‗‗‗‗‗‗‗‗‗‗‗‗‗‗‗‗‗‗‗‗‗‗‗‗‗

‗‗‗‗‗‗‗‗‗‗‗‗‗‗‗‗‗‗‗‗‗‗‗‗‗‗‗‗‗‗‗‗‗‗‗‗‗‗‗‗‗‗‗‗‗‗‗

‗‗‗‗‗‗‗‗‗‗‗‗‗‗‗‗‗‗‗‗‗‗‗‗‗‗‗‗‗‗‗‗‗‗‗‗‗‗‗‗‗‗‗‗‗‗‗

‗‗‗‗‗‗‗‗‗‗‗‗‗‗‗‗‗‗‗‗‗‗‗‗‗‗‗‗‗‗‗‗‗‗‗‗‗‗‗‗‗‗‗‗‗‗‗

Recorded by: ‗‗‗‗‗‗‗‗‗‗‗‗‗‗‗‗‗‗‗‗‗‗‗‗‗

# APPENDIX E

**Common and scientific names used in the text—**

## Plants

### Trees

| Common Name | Scientific Name |
|---|---|
| Alpine fir | *Abies lasiocarpa* (Hook.) Nutt. |
| Apple | *Malus spp.* |
| Aspen | *Populus tremuloides* Michx. |
| Balsam fir | *Abies balsamea* Mill |
| Bigleaf maple | *Acer macrophylla* Pursh |
| Black cottonwood | *Populus tricocarpa* Torr. & Gray |
| Bitter cherry | *Prunus emarginata* Dougl. |
| Cascara | *Rhamnus purshiana* |
| Douglas-fir | *Psuedotsuga menziesii* (Mirb.) Franco |
| Elderberry | *Sambucus spp.* |
| Engelmann spruce | *Picea englemanni* (Parry) Engelm |
| Grand fir | *Abies grandis* (Dougl.) Lindl. |
| Larch | *Larix occidentalis* Nutt. |
| Lodgepole pine | *Pinus contorta* Dougl. |
| Noble fir | *Abies procera* Rehd. |
| Oso-berry (Indian plum) | *Osmaronia cerasiformis* (T. & G.) Greene |
| Ponderosa pine | *Pinus ponderosa* Laws. |
| Red alder | *Alnus rubra* Bong. |
| Red spruce | *Picea rubens* Link. |
| Redwood | *Sequoia sempervirens* (D. Don) Endl. |
| Silver fir | *Abies amabilis* (Dougl.) Forbes |
| Sitka spruce | *Picea sitchensis* (Bong.) Carr |
| Vine maple | *Acer circinatum* Pursh |
| Western hemlock | *Tsuga heterophylla* Sarg. |
| Western redcedar | *Thuja plicata* Donn |
| White cedar | *Thuja occidentalis/Cupressus thyoides* L. |
| White pine | *Pinus monticola* Dougl. |
| White spruce | *Picea glauca* Voss. |
| Whitebark pine | *Pinus albicaulis* Engelm. |
| Willow | *Salix spp.* |

### Shrubs

|  |  |
|---|---|
| Devil's club | *Opolopanax horridum* (J. E. Smith) Miq. |
| Huckleberry | *Vaccinium spp.* |
| Oceanspray | *Holodiscus discolor* (Pursh) Maxim. |
| Oregon grape | *Berberis nervosa* Pursh |
| Rubus spp. | *Rubus spp.* |
| Salal | *Gautheria shallon* Pursh |
| Salmonberry | *Rubus spectabilis* Pursh |

| Common Name | Fungi<br>Scientific Name |
|---|---|
| Fungi | *Armillaria mellea* |
| | *Ceratocystis piceae* |
| | *Fomes annosus* |
| | *Fomes cajanderi* |
| | *Fomes pinicola* |
| | *Odontia bicolor* |
| | *Polyporus schweinitzii* |
| | *Stereum sanguinolentum* |
| | *Trametes serialis* |

## Other

| | |
|---|---|
| Bedstraw | *Galium spp.* |
| Bracken fern | *Pteridium aquilinum* (L.) Kuhn |
| Clover | *Trifolium spp.* |
| Deer fern | *Struthiopteris spicant* |
| False dandelion | *Hypochareris radicata* L. |
| Grasses | *Graminae* |
| Horsetail | *Equisetum spp.* |
| Oxalis | *Oxalis oregana* Nutt. ex T. & G. |
| Sedges | *Carex spp.* |
| Skunk cabbage | *Lysichitium americanum* Hult & St. John |
| Strawberry | *Fragaria spp.* |
| Sword fern | *Polystichum munitum* (Kaulf.) Presl |
| Waterleaf | *Hydrophyllum spp.* |
| Woodrush | *Luzula spp.* |

## Animals

### Mammals

| | |
|---|---|
| Black bear | *Ursus americanus* Pallus |
| Black bear | *U. a. altifrontalis* Elliot |
| Black bear | *U. a. cinnamomum* Audubon & Bachman |
| Chickaree | *Tamiasciurus douglasii* Bachman |
| Grizzly bear | *U. arctos* Linnaeus |
| Moose | *Alces alces* Linnaeus |
| Polar bear | *Thalarctos maritimus* Phipps |
| Porcupine | *Erithizon dorsatum* Linnaeus |

### Miscellaneous Vertebrates

| | |
|---|---|
| Pacific giant salamander | *Dicamptodon ensatus* Eschscholtz |
| Redside shiner | *Richardsonius balteatus* Richardson |
| Reticulate, sculpin | *Cottus perplexus* Gilbert & Evermann |
| River lampreys | *Lampetra spp.* |
| Salmon | *Oncorhynchus spp.* |
| Trout | *Salmo spp.* |

179

| Common Name | Scientific Name |
|---|---|
| **Insects** | |
| Carpenter ant | *Camponotus herculeanus* |
| Dampwood termite | *Zootermuosis anusticollis* |
| **External Parasites** | |
| Flea | *Arctopsylla ursi* |
| Lice | *Trichodectes sp., T. pinguis* |
| Ticks | *Ixodes sp., Dermacentor andersoni* |
| **Internal Parasites** | |
| Fluke | *Nanophyetus salmincola* |
| Hookworm | *Uncinaria yukonensis* |
| Infectious agent of N. salmincola | *Neorickettsia helminthoeca* |
| Lungworm | *Crenosoma sp.* |
| Roundworm | *Dirofilaria ursi, Toxascaris sp.* |
| Tapeworm | *Taenia saginata* |